1—C.Q.

Clever Queen

Clever Queen

A Tale of the Jungle and of Devil Worshipers

by
Eric B. Hare

Illustrated by
John Steel

PACIFIC PRESS PUBLISHING ASSOCIATION
MOUNTAIN VIEW, CALIFORNIA
OMAHA, NEBRASKA
OSHAWA, ONTARIO

Contents

CHAPTER I

Born Among the Devil Worshipers

"**D**RAW the curtains tight, put some wood on the fire, and, remember, she's to drink no water but a drop or two as she dips her finger in," said Grandma to a woman helper squatting near by. She lowered her finger after giving the command, then slowly went out to the veranda, and, sitting on a mat, as cool and as collected as if nothing at all had happened, beamed upon the few friends waiting there, and simply said, "It's a girl."

"A girl!" they chorused and smiled, for girl babies are always as welcome as boys in Our Jungle.

"Ugh, a girl!" grunted Grandma, "and she's very fair, too." Then taking down a few threads of cotton that hung in strands from a bamboo, almost ready for weaving into clothes or blankets, she began to twist them into a strong string about eighteen inches long.

"You'll have to give the devils a sacrifice for that!" said one.

"Indeed, I shall that!" said Grandma. "I shall that! But first I'll tie the string and say a prayer. It pays, you know;" and, dropping her voice to a whisper, added, "it pays not to make the devils angry."

"Ugh! Ugh! Ugh!" grunted the friends in assent. "It does that! It does that!"

1

And so they sat and talked and grunted till the string was done. Then going inside the curtains again, Grandma tied the string loosely around the little baby's neck, and prayed:

> "Spirit of the water, spirit of the land,
> Spirit of the rivers, spirit of the forest,
> This little baby will pray to you,
> This little baby will sacrifice to you.
> So keep away your sorrow and sickness;
> Keep away your plague and death."

Grandma sighed as she came out of the curtained room, not only because she felt that her responsibility to the devils was well begun, but also because it was hot in there. It was hot enough outside, but the custom of the devil worshipers demanded that not a breath of air blow on the mother or baby for seven days, lest they should catch cold; so it just had to be done. And for seven long days that poor mother with her little babe sighed and sweltered and longed for the time when she could see outside and breathe fresh air again.

At last the seven days were over, the curtain was lifted, and the mother was allowed to walk around the house. From a shelf near the waterpot she took a small earthen pot, in which nothing had ever been cooked before. She washed it, then filled it with rice and water, and put it on the fire to cook.

When it was nicely done, one spoonful was placed on the spirit altar, which is a kind of shelf nailed onto one of the house posts, and the little brass bell that was hanging nearby was rung. This was to call the attention of the spirits to the offering, of course. And then, what do you think the mother did with the rest of the rice? That was to be her little baby girl's first rice dinner!

"But the baby didn't have any teeth, and how could she eat rice?" I can hear you say.

Well, don't you think I know that? So did her mother. She knew the baby couldn't chew rice; so, sitting down with the baby in her lap and a pot of rice by her side, the mother took some of the rice in her fingers, and put it, not into the baby's mouth, but into her own mouth. Then she chewed, and chewed, and chewed, till it was soft and slobbery, and then she poked it right into her little baby's mouth.

Of course the baby didn't like it, and spat it out, and the mother had to poke it in again; and as she poked and chewed, and chewed and poked, she sang:

> "Eat rice, little queen,
> And don't be mean;
> Eat rice, eat rice,
> And grow up nice."

You are horrified to think of feeding rice to little babies only a week old, even if it is chewed up first. In fact, that makes it more horrible still. But Grandma sat looking proudly on, quite satisfied with what was happening. She well remembered how she had fed all her babies their first dinner of rice, and was quite sure that was the reason why three out of six had lived.

She had great faith in the string around the little baby's neck too. Later on, different kinds of charms would be tied to this string; but, for the present, now that the baby had had its first meal of rice, she grunted approvingly, and went down the bamboo ladder to feed the chickens.

As she came back up the steps, the baby's mother sat smiling and cooing with her little one in her arms.

"Oh, Grandma," she cried, "did you ever see a baby so clever? She is looking at me, Grandma. She can see me!" And squeezing the baby up tight, she said, "Mother's clever little darling!" (You know how mothers talk to their wee babies.) And she kept on saying, "Mother's clever little baby girl! Mother's little clever queen! Oh, yes, that's it, mother's little clever queen!"

Then she stopped quickly, for a new thought had come to her, and, turning, she said to the grandma, "Why, we haven't named the baby yet, Grandma! We haven't named the baby yet! But I know what I shall name her. It shall be 'Clever Queen,' 'Clever Queen'— Yes, it shall be 'Clever Queen.' Do you hear, little baby? Your name is Clever Queen."

"Ugh! Ugh!" grunted Grandma; "the name is good."

I don't suppose you would like to have a name like that, would you? But over in Burma the Karen devil worshipers wouldn't think of calling a little girl Betty Jane or Polly Anne; they are always called by some character name. So a nice little fat baby might be called Miss Fat. If she is fair, she might be called Miss White. If a baby cries a lot, she might be called Miss Cry Hard. If the baby sleeps well, she might be called Miss Sleep Sweet or Miss Good Girl. If a baby is very pretty, a fancy name combining the name of a flower with the name of a precious stone is often used; and we hear such names as Miss Transparent Gold or Miss Victorious Diamond. This little girl was given the name Clever Queen.

We can't help but feel sorry for the little children who are born among the devil worshipers. We know that it is only God and the angels who can protect us. But Clever Queen's Grandma did not know how to worship God; she had worshiped the devils all her life and was doing the best she knew so that little Clever Queen would grow up into a very beautiful and diligent young woman.

Famine in the Village

GRANDMA sat on the floor, tugging at a piece of bark rope tied to a hammock, swinging little Clever Queen to and fro, to and fro. The rice that had been fed to the baby had given her the hiccups; but that didn't matter, for Grandma knew exactly what to do. She tore off a little piece of paper about as big as a postage stamp and, licking it, stuck it on Clever Queen's forehead. Then, quickly putting her back into the hammock, she vigorously pulled it to and fro while she sang:

"The chickens are scratching at the fireplace,
So shut your eyes and do not weep.
When you grow up, you'll be cooking rice.
Now close your eyes, and go to sleep."

And, believe it or not, the hiccups stopped, and soon little Clever Queen was fast asleep.

We cannot take time to tell you all that happened in the early months of this little baby girl's life. Like all other little babies, she ate and slept and cried. She was loved and cuddled and carried around, and so the hot weeks and months of the dry season passed quickly. By the time Clever Queen was beginning to cut her first teeth, big black clouds rolled up into the sky, and the wet season began. It rained

5

and it rained so heavily that for weeks she didn't get outside to watch the pigs and the chickens and the ducks downstairs. The chickens must have been lonely too, as well as wet, for they often came up into the house and, after looking at the little baby first out of one eye and then out of the other—you know how cunning little chickens can be —they would run over to the fireplace, and preen their feathers, and open out their wings to dry. So Clever Queen was happy enough even if she did have to stay indoors. But Grandma and Mother were sad.

Other black clouds were rolling over them. Not rain clouds, but trouble clouds; for there had been so much rain that the rice fields had been flooded. And now if the flood didn't go down quickly, their rice would all die, and they had no more seed.

"Let's sacrifice a pig," said Grandma; "then perhaps the devils will let the water go down."

So Grandma and Clever Queen's daddy called two uncles and aunties to sleep in their house three days. Then they roasted a pig and, sitting around it before feasting on it, they prayed:

> "O devil, here's a pig for you!
> O water spirit, here's a pig for you!
> Call off the flood, take away the water,
> Let our rice grow, let our food grow."

But the flood kept up as high as ever.

"Let's sacrifice a chicken," said Grandma; "maybe the devil wants a chicken."

So they did the same thing with a chicken, and prayed:

> "O devil, here's a chicken for you!
> O water spirit, here's a chicken for you!
> Call off the flood, take away the water,
> Let our rice grow, let our food grow."

But the flood kept up as high as ever, and by this time their rice was all dead.

What sad people they were! And don't you feel sorry for them? The very greatest sadness is among people who do not know God and who sacrifice to devils. In spite of all their sacrifices, an awful famine came in their village.

In just a month or two all the last year's rice would be finished, and there would be nothing else to eat. So Grandpa and Daddy sharpened their big heavy knives, and started off over the hills to the bamboo forests, hoping to cut bamboos and sell them, and thus get money with which to buy rice.

They were gone such a long time that Grandma did not know what to do; so she caught a pig, and, tying its legs together, she put it in a canoe and went down the river to a village about twelve miles away where she traded it for some rice. She was glad to be able to bring back something to eat; but her happiness didn't last long. There were only a few more pigs, and there were many more months before the next year's rice would be ready; and how long would it be before Grandpa and Daddy came back? And what were they going to do when their last pig was gone? And without pigs how would they be able to sacrifice to the devils?

Grandma shut her eyes, and tried not to think as she tugged at the swing where little Clever Queen slept.

"Oh, little Clever Queen," she sobbed, "whatever will happen to you? Will your daddy never come back? Oh, what shall we do when the pigs are all gone?"

And, in spite of herself, Grandma shuddered at the thought of the awful famine that had befallen them.

Poor Grandma was a devil worshiper, and she was afraid. Of course, we have the promise of God that in famine, "bread shall be given" us and our "water shall be sure"; but Grandma didn't know God.

CHAPTER 3

Sold for
Two Bags of Rice

AT LAST the day came when there was only one pig left, and as Grandma floated down the river with it in her canoe, she was more worried and anxious than ever. Yet she tried not to cry, because the devil worshipers are not supposed to let the devils know how they feel inside. So as she paddled her canoe she sang to herself:

> "Spirit of the river,
>> Speed me on my way!
> Spirit of the paddy,
>> Bring me good fortune today!"

And she sang and she sang, till at last she reached the village where she was going to trade her last pig for some paddy or rice.

Some boys who were playing on the riverbank helped Grandma lift her pig onto her back; and, as they did so, they said, "Grandma, go quickly to the house beyond the buffalo pen, straight up there by the coconut tree. We heard the man say just this morning that they wished they had a pig, for their little baby is sick, and they have sacrificed with chickens; but it seems that the devils don't want chickens, so these people wished they had a pig."

Grandma grunted her thanks and hastened in the direction that the boys had pointed out; but as she got close, her heart sank within her, for the terrible wailing that reached her ears told her more than she wanted to know just then.

"Oh, Grandma, you're too late, you're too late!" wailed the poor mother. "Why didn't you come with your pig yesterday? Maybe the devils would have been satisfied, and spared the life of my little baby; but now my Pretty Diamond is dead! Oh! oh!" and the poor mother wailed and wailed dreadfully, as only heathen mothers can wail.

As she cried, Grandma tried to comfort her. "Oh," she said, "what a world this is indeed! Oh, how terrible to be slaves of the devils! Here's you, with plenty to eat, and your baby's taken; and there's us with famine, and not knowing where we can get the next bite to feed our little Clever Queen."

"Your baby—Clever Queen?" sobbed the heartbroken mother. "Nothing to eat?—A baby?—How many moons?"

"Our Clever Queen is nine months old this new moon," said Grandma; "but with not enough to eat, her poor mother can't feed her at the breast, and her life is truly full of trouble."

"Nine moons! Nine moons! Mine was only eight; but one more moon wouldn't matter. Give her to me! Bring her to me! Grandma, do you hear? I'll give you rice. I'll give you money. I'll give you *anything!* Bring me your Clever Queen."

Grandma's heart was beating fast. Had she not prayed for good fortune that day? Was this—could this be the will of the spirits?

The sad mother who had lost her little baby saw Grandma hesitate. "Go now and bring her to me!" she cried. "Leave here your pig, and we will care for it for you. Go quickly, Grandma; my dead baby's father will go with you to help you paddle your canoe. Only go! go! go! And come again quickly!" And, hardly knowing why she did it, Grandma

2—C.Q.

Grandma paddled back home across the river. She carried in her boat the two bags of rice for which she had traded Clever Queen.

turned and followed the poor woman's husband down to
the canoe, and by evening they were back at Grandma's
village.

"I'll give you two bags of rice, Grandma. Rice, not
paddy," said the father, as he walked toward the house. Up
the ladder they scrambled, and without waiting a moment,
Grandma, all excited, told the poor, sick, hungry mother
all that had happened that day.

Clever Queen's mother hesitated a moment, then nodded
her assent as she said slowly, "She'll die anyway if we have
no food. Take her, and she will live." In her heart she knew
that if fortune turned she would buy her back some day;
but now—yes, it seemed best.

"I'll go and stay in my uncle's house," she simply added;
"you may go while I'm away."

We cannot imagine the feelings of the poor mother as,
with a look of pain, she took one glance at her darling
little baby and then fled to the other side of the village
that she might not hear her cry. Nor can we fully understand the great joy of the other mother when, before morning, she cuddled little Clever Queen to her breast. Little
Clever Queen had been sold for two bags of rice!

CHAPTER 4

The Famine Ends

CLEVER QUEEN'S new mother was just as kind as kind could be. Oh, how she loved her new baby, and cuddled her! And although I am sure little Clever Queen missed her own mother, with plenty to drink she at once became happy and contented.

> "They stole my Pretty Diamond;
> They were horrible and mean.
> But I've got another darling,
> And her name is Clever Queen,"

the new mother sang as she swung the child to sleep in the hammock so that she could cook the evening meal.

> "We offered them our chickens;
> They were horrible and mean.
> Yes, they stole my Pretty Diamond,
> But they'll not get Clever Queen!"

But away up in the village where the famine was, Clever Queen's sadhearted mother was singing a prayer:

> "Good Spirit of forest and water,
> Go follow my dear little daughter;
> She's the best that ever was seen.
> Oh, care for my own Clever Queen!

"We sold her for two bags of rice;
But she's not gone away to stay.
When her father has sold his bamboos,
We'll buy her back some day."

And all this time the baby's own grandpa and father were cutting their bamboos away up in the mountains. They dragged them ten at a time to a little creek and then tied five bundles together, making fifty in a larger bundle. These they floated down to the big river and hid them among the bushes. In this way they worked till they had two thousand bamboos, all tied in bundles of fifty. They had to float them down the river to the city before they could sell them; so, when at last they had sold their bamboos and were ready to come back to their village, several months had passed away. The dismal rainy season was gone, and with it the flood. In other districts the rice was already reaped, and there were signs of a plentiful harvest.

So what did it matter now? They had money. They could buy rice. They could buy enough for Grandma and Mother and Clever Queen, if—if they were still alive! The dreadful thought made them hasten. Well they knew that famines are terrible things. But they knew that Grandma was very old and very wise, and they hoped that she had been able to find a way out. So silently they hastened on through the jungle, staying only long enough to sleep a little and to eat. And one evening before the sun was set, they came to their house.

Grandma was downstairs pounding paddy. She stopped a moment; and opened her mouth in surprise, but she spoke no word as she saw the men walk into the house. The devil worshipers dare not show their happiness for fear that the spirits may visit their displeasure on some loved one. Upstairs, too, Clever Queen's mother stopped cooking rice only long enough to be sure who these two men coming into the house were. And then, as though they had been away only for a day, she went on with her work, without a word.

The men threw their bundles of clothes and bedding to the floor, walked over to the waterpot, washed their feet and hands, and then only asked, "Is the rice cooked?"

"All cooked," was the answer. And while his wife dished up the rice, Clever Queen's father looked into the bedroom to see if his little daughter were there. Not finding her anywhere in the house, he concluded she was dead; and, though it made him sad, he dared not say anything about it. To talk about it would only make him sadder.

His wife, now realizing that they had money and that the famine would mean nothing more to them, was ashamed to think that she had sold their baby, and dared not say anything. So they ate in silence. By and by, sitting by the fire at night, he asked, "You have rice?"

"Plenty for several more weeks," his wife replied.

"How come?" he continued.

"Pigs," was the reply. "But have you money?" whispered the wife.

"Plenty."

"But *lots* of it?"

"Why all these questions? Do you not fear that someone will hear?"

"Nay, I fear nothing. Only how I hope you have enough to buy back our Clever Queen!"

"Buy—back—our—Clever—Queen!" was all he said; but he understood all. And, standing up, he walked out into the night.

How sorry we feel for the poor people in the jungle who are afraid to be happy, and afraid to be sad, and who live in fear of the devils! Do you suppose that as Clever Queen's father walked around that night, he decided to buy her back?

CHAPTER **5**

Stolen Back Again

DOWN the track Daddy walked. Through the bamboos; past his paddy field. He did not know where he wanted to go, but he kept on going, and as he went, he thought, "Sold! Sold! Oh," he groaned, "why didn't they wait till I got back! Oh, but of course then they would all have been dead. She's sold—but she's still alive! That's better, after all, than being dead. And I have money; ha, of course, I'll buy her back! But—they might ask all my money; and then—then we would all have to starve. Buy her back? No, that wouldn't do! Buy her back?—isn't there some other way?"

To his agonized heart there came a thought. Quick, like a flash, it stopped his walking. It made his heart go pitter-patter. Why couldn't he steal her back? Ha, why couldn't he? People stole pigs, people stole bullocks; why couldn't he steal a baby? Why? Why? Why? He turned and ran. If there were tigers, he cared not for them. If there were snakes, it mattered not. Even the darkness mattered not; this was his village, and he was familiar with every track, every stone, and every tree. He paused only as he neared the village, so that his hurry would not arouse the slumberings dogs. His plans called for quietness.

Quietly, stealthily, he reached his ladder and climbed up into his house. He paused till his eyes got used to the darkness; and, even as he paused, he heard a smothered

15

sob. Turning toward the fireplace, he was more than satisfied to find his wife still sitting there, her face faintly lit up
by the glow of the dying embers.

"So she too is thinking! Good!" he breathed to himself;
then, noticing that no one else was there to hear or to listen,
he sat down beside her, and whispered into her ear, "We
cannot buy back our—"

"Oh, husband, say not that we cannot buy back our
Clever Queen or else my heart will break!" sobbed his poor
wife.

"Wait, listen! Do not speak till you have heard all. I say
we cannot buy back our Clever Queen, for then we shall all
starve. For know, O woman, that by this time she, too, loves
our Clever Queen, and she will ask all the money that I
have; and then wherewith shall we buy food even for our
babe?"

The body of his poor wife shook as she tried to smother
her choking sobs. But she said nothing. What *could* she
say? "Listen, I, Clever Queen's father, have thought of a
better plan," continued her husband. "If you will but agree,
there is nothing at all to stop us from *stealing* back our
babe."

The sobs stopped as if by magic. A restless hand began
to stir the smoldering sticks in the fire. A frightened face
looked toward the man, and trembling lips began to say,
"You mean—you mean—"

"I mean exactly what I have said. Don't people steal
pigs? Don't people steal bullocks? Why do you sit here
sobbing? Come. Let us go."

A moment longer she sat there. Then wiping her eyes
with her shawl, she arose quietly, and said, "We will go."

The morning dawned bright and fair in the village where
Clever Queen lived with her new mother. The old grandma
of this home was up early and, with a basket on her back

and a net in her hand, was off to a near-by pond to catch some prawns for breakfast. The men had gone to their clearing in the jungle, and the mother, with Clever Queen tied to her back, was pounding rice under the house. For this is what all good Jungle people do.

The chickens were scratching, the ducks were quacking, the pigs were grunting, the dogs were running around, and little children were playing here and there, when up from the river there came a stranger.

The dogs barked furiously and ran toward him, but he just said, "*Twe! Twe!*" which they recognized as their own language for dog, and they at once quieted down. Slowly he walked, yet like one knowing where he was going, up past the buffalo pen; and there near the coconut tree he saw what he wanted!—A woman pounding paddy with a baby tied on her back; and he heard what he wanted, for he caught the last of her song:

> "They were horrible and mean.
> But I've got another darling,
> And her name is Clever Queen."

"Auntie, what are you doing?" he greeted her.

"Nothing," she replied.

"Do you have any rice to sell?"

"No."

"But I've got money. Silver. For you have heard that the famine is bad up the river. And I have cut bamboos and sold them in the city," continued the stranger. (Have you guessed who the stranger was?) "See. My money. Hear it jingle!"

"Oh, well—that's different! For money. Yes, of course we will sell a little paddy, for we need to buy cloth and needles. Come to the paddy barn, over there near the buffalo pen." And, undoing the sheet that tied Clever Queen to her back, she put her in the hammock, asleep, and hurried to uncover the rice and to measure out the quantity the stranger wanted.

Things like this happen so seldom that the buying of the rice soon gathered quite a crowd. It took a long time too, for the stranger had much to tell of things he had seen in the city; so that there was plenty of time for Clever Queen's real mother, who was hidden in the bushes behind the house, to run to the hammock, and steal back her own baby. Hastily she tied Clever Queen to her back and then fled silently and unseen into the jungle.

All this time Clever Queen's father talked and talked and laughed and laughed, for he wanted all attention to be taken from the house where the mother was taking away little Clever Queen; but at last, feeling sure that there had been plenty of time, he shouldered his bag, and simply said, "I'm going."

Slowly he walked down through the village, and putting his bag into the canoe, was just about to start off, when a terrible scream was heard in the village. Fearing that if he went off too quickly he might arouse their suspicions, he hastened back with the others in the direction of the screaming.

"They've taken her! They've taken her!" screamed the poor mother, who had just missed Clever Queen. "They've taken her! They've taken her!"

"Taken whom?" asked the stranger, as coolly as he could.

"My Clever Queen!" was the sad reply. Then between cries and screams, they told him the story of Pretty Diamond's death, and how they had bought Clever Queen with two bags of rice, and how they loved her. "And now she's gone too! She's gone too!" screamed the woman.

"Ah, I've seen such things before," comforted the stranger. "Yes, it's the spirits all right! 'Tis a bad world that we live in! Famine and death and devils. But, just to be sure, we'd better look around a bit. You send some of the folks over toward the hills, and send some down the river; and I'll help you too. I'm going up the river, and I'll keep my eyes open and ask wherever I can."

"Please do," sobbed the terrified woman, "and come back quickly if there's news!"

Now that there was no suspicion attached to him, he ran to his canoe and paddled for dear life up the river. Up, up. "Has Clever Queen's mother been able to make it?" he asked himself, as he neared the place where she was to meet him. For a moment his heart nearly stopped as he caught no sight or sound of anyone. But even as his canoe grounded on the sand, the bushes parted, and, triumphant, Clever Queen's own mother stepped into the canoe, with her own Clever Queen in her arms!

CHAPTER **6**

Under the
Spell of Magic

UP THE river in their canoe they paddled, happy
and triumphant; but their happiness didn't last
long. Their excited talking gave way to long periods of
silence.

The mother started, as a little eddy rocked their canoe,
and she gasped, "I'm afraid already!"

"Nay, fear not," answered her husband. "They think it
is the spirits; and I have already helped by telling them to
look down the river, while I look up the river; and now we
have our Clever Queen, and we have money. What is there
to fear?"

"But where shall we go?"

"Ah, that, too, I have thought out. Is it not time to clear
the jungle on the sides of the mountains for next year's rice
crop? Did not our rice die last year in the flood? But do
the floods cover the hills? Then this year we shall clear a
patch of jungle on the side of a hill, and when it is dry, we
will burn it, and in the ashes we will grow good rice which
the floods cannot kill. And I shall take you and the babe to
the hills, and build for you a little hut, right there. After
many days and weeks, people will hear, but not quickly.
And by that time, the heart of Pretty Diamond's mother
will be healed, and she will not want our Clever Queen
anymore."

The mother nodded. "Your plans are good," she said simply and, taking up her paddle, helped to paddle the canoe upstream.

But away back in the village from where the babe had been stolen, the mother without a babe still cried. Her husband had tried to comfort her, but it was no use. The searchers came back without any news, and, at last, giving up hope, Pretty Diamond's mother cried out, " 'Tis the work of devils! 'Tis the work of devils! Bring me the devil doctor. Go bring me the devil doctor."

It had been an exciting day. And now everyone crowded around. Mothers clutched their babies, lest the spirits might steal them away too, and all waited anxiously to see if the devil doctor would come. But he had been called away to attend some other case in a village far away. It looked as if the crying and the screaming would start all over again, when Old Grandma stepped forward.

"What does it matter if the doctor is away?" she said. "Do we not also understand the customs of the spirits, and can we not also ask them to pity us, and can we not also cast a spell, and smite with magic? Bring me now some of the baby's clothes, and some of its food, and some of its water, and listen now to me." Then she scraped off a little bit of dirt from the clothes and put it in her hands, added a little of the baby's rice and a little water, and worked the mass round and round in the palm of her hands, muttering all the time, and blowing in on it occasionally. Then quickly putting it in her mouth and blowing it out with all her force, she called out:

> "Go smite with sickness, go smite with sores,
> Go high, go low, go in, go out!
> Go up, go down, go north, go south,
> From the water, from the forest,
> From the rice field, from the house,
> Bring back, bring back our Clever Queen."

It all seemed very mystifying. And it seemed to bring some degree of comfort to the sorrowing mother. The village people grunted their approval and quickly dispersed. And soon frightened faces gathered around the different fireplaces, where in hushed tones they told and retold stories of the wrath of the devils.

Up on the side of the mountain, as Clever Queen's father hastily cut his bamboos to build his little house, her mother tied a cotton blanket hammock-like between two little trees, and, putting her baby in it, tried to swing her to sleep. But there was clearly something the matter. Clever Queen only cried and cried. She was over a year old now, and had been living with her new mother for about four months. There she had had plenty of milk to drink in addition to the rice she could now eat; but here on the mountainside, though she had her real mother, she had no milk, and she was not happy at all. In vain her mother tried to coax her to eat—a little rice, a little banana. But no, she would do nothing but cry, cry, cry, till at last, exhausted, she fell asleep.

Hastily the mother put a few stones together, and began to make a fire to cook the afternoon rice, and all this time the little bamboo hut was quickly taking shape. Nine little poles, in three rows about four feet apart, with forks about four feet from the ground, did not take long to place. Then in the forks were tied three bamboos like rafters. Across these were placed about fifty other bamboos for the floor. Then three more bamboo poles tied to the top of the house posts, with the middle one about eight feet above the floor and the two side ones about two feet above the floor, made the rafters for the roof, and soon it was all done but tying the leaf thatch onto the roof bamboos. But this would take much time as the leaves would have to be gathered and sewed on bamboo strips first; so for the first night the father simply threw over the hut a few branches, and the house was ready.

Before the rice was cooked, however, Clever Queen was awake and crying again. "I'm afraid her kalar is lost," moaned her mother. ("Kalar" is what the Jungle people call their spirits.) "Yes, I'm afraid her kalar is lost," she repeated to her husband as he came to eat. "Before we go up into the house, you had better try to find it. Here, take a little offering—some rice, some tobacco—and do it now before the darkness comes upon us."

Hastily splitting a bamboo into thin strips, the father wove a little bamboo basket to hold the offering, and a larger one in which to catch the kalar. Then going into the jungle not far away, he hung the offering on a little tree, and called out:

> "Come back, Kalar, come back!
>   Come back, Kalar, come back!
>   Kalar, Kalar, can't you find the way?
>   Over here, over here, Kalar! Kalar!
>   Come up from the village, come up from the river!
>   Come right up the trail, up here on the hill!
>   Come back, Kalar, come back!"

Then, as if imagining the spirit had heard him, he danced around, here and there, sweeping through the air with his basket, behind this tree, behind that one, now running here, now dodging there, as if he were playing tag with some unseen friend; then, hastily closing his basket after one mighty swoop, he cried out triumphantly, "Here it is! I've got it!" and ran back to his hut.

The mother, smiling, caught up her babe in her arms. "It's all right now! it's all right now, my Clever Queen!" she said, "your kalar has come back. Come, Father has it in the basket; let us go to the house." And saying this, she followed her husband up the ladder into the hut.

Father danced around, sweeping through the air with his little basket, as he tried to catch poor Clever Queen's lost spirit.

But kalar or no kalar, the baby kept on crying, sleeping only in snatches through the night. And often through the night the mother whispered to the husband, "I'm afraid— I'm afraid—I'm afraid that Pretty Diamond's mother has cursed us. See how the little one starts, and cries."

"Nay, fear not, is she not ours?" the husband replied. He tried to make his voice sound brave, but it trembled, and, instead of comforting his wife, made her all the more fearful.

"But look! Listen! It is! It is! See that movement in her little stomach! Look at her half-closed eyes. Husband, it is! It is! We are cursed!" his wife replied. And, believe it or not, the next day Clever Queen was very sick with a high fever. For three days she was sick, and the fear of the parents grew until they were both so terrified that they jumped and started even at the ordinary sounds of the forest. Then sores broke out on the little one's leg, and in spite of the parents' spitting on leaves and sticking the leaves on the sores (which is the recognized Jungle way of treating all sores), the sores spread and spread and got bigger and bigger till the little baby was in a terrible condition.

"Oh, husband," moaned the mother, "it's no use! We are cursed! We are cursed! And here in the jungle, with no pigs or chickens to sacrifice, what hope have we of fighting off the curse? Let us be going."

"Let us be going where?" answered the husband. "If we go to the village, they will find us. If we go farther into the jungle, it will be worse. If we stay here, she'll die. Tell me, where shall we go? I am ready to take you anywhere."

"Husband," she said, "there is only one thing we can do. It has come to me in my dreams; even the birds as they sing seem to say it. 'Take her back, take her back,' they say. We must! We must! We must take her back!"

Darkness came down over the hillside that night, and into the little bamboo hut where the mother sat crying with

3—C.Q.

her sick babe in her arms, and found them all ready to start on another journey in the morning.

You cannot imagine the fear of those who worship devils. I don't believe in magic or curses; nor do you. I've seen many things in my dispensary which they said were the result of magic, but I know them to be only symptoms of sickness and disease. But it doesn't matter what you and I think and know. The devil worshipers do believe in magic, and it does seem to have a great power over them.

But I want to tell you that the name of Jesus and the presence of the holy angels are much more powerful than that of the devils. I've lived in the Jungle for twenty years, and I have never been troubled with any curse or magic. And I am glad to say that no matter how much trouble the devil worshipers may have had in the past, when they become Christians, they, too, are freed from the power and the fear of the devils.

CHAPTER 7

With the Pigs
Under the House

THE few miles to where the canoe was kept in the mouth of a little stream which emptied into the big river were soon traveled, and as Clever Queen's mother took her place in the canoe she smiled for the first time.

"Look, she sleeps," she said to her husband; "we are doing right. It is fate! It is fate! We cannot do anything against fate."

The journey down the river was easy, and by the time the sun was halfway down to the horizon, the mother was carefully and silently working her way through the jungle toward the village from which she had stolen her own child. She dared not travel by the frequented paths, so her progress was slow; but at last she could see the village, and then the very house to which she must take the babe. How could she tell whether anyone was home or not?

But it was easy to tell. There was smoke coming from the house. Yes, there were people at home. So she waited and waited. As she waited, the baby cried, and, fearing that someone could hear, she put her hand over the baby's mouth and fled in terror. Then by the time the baby slept again there were still signs that the people were home.

At last darkness came, and still there had been no chance

to put the baby back in the house. She watched and watched till the fading lights told that the people had gone to sleep. Then, holding her breath and hugging Clever Queen near her throbbing heart, she crept closer and closer.

She had reached the house; but still what could she do? How could she—what could she do? The ladder was drawn up onto the veranda. She might have known it would be thus—all Jungle folks do that to stop people coming unheard into their houses at night. And she couldn't leave the babe downstairs! But why couldn't she? And as she thought of it, she looked—and there, almost within reach, lay a big mother pig with her litter of baby pigs all snuggled in together.

"Oh," she thought, "that mother pig wouldn't mind another baby for a little while; and it will not be long before the babe will cry and let them know she is there." Would she? Could she?

"Yes, it has to be done," the poor frightened mother said half aloud to herself. "The curse of the spirits is upon me; it has to be done. And not daring to begin to argue with herself, she leaned over and placed little Clever Queen under the house among the pigs.

The little pigs squirmed; the big pig grunted; a dog barked. The mother, trying to flee, quickened her steps into a run. More dogs barked, more pigs grunted. It was no use being quiet now; and, fearing only that she would be caught by the villagers as a thief, she ran for dear life.

"*Twe! Twe! Twe*" came from two or three men at once, as they tried to quiet the dogs. But the dogs had heard real footsteps, and would not be quieted; they barked louder and louder. Convinced that there must be something the matter, several men got up to investigate.

There was a baby crying. Where was it? Where? Down under a house! Could it have fallen out? Two men seized

The cry of a baby awakened the villagers. Two men took a bamboo torch and found Clever Queen crying among the little pigs.

a bamboo torch and soon found Clever Queen among the little pigs.

"Aye, whose baby?" called the men.

"Baby?" "Which baby?" "Where?" In a minute men were answering men, and mothers were counting babies.

"Say, Pretty Diamond's mother, come look under your house. Have the spirits brought back your Clever Queen?"

Spirits! Clever Queen! The excitement was so great that all thought of following the footsteps which long before this had disappeared, was forgotten. The whole village was astir. Mothers crowded around with their babes in their arms, as the men pointed out the mother pig and the very place where they had found the baby. The dogs added confusion by barking their loudest; while frightened, sleepy boys and girls ran here and there, wondering what it was all about.

Old Grandma, who had cast the spell, grunted her triumph. "Aye! It is! It is! It's our Clever Queen! Aha! They've brought her back, they have! The devils have surely helped us this time! Well, they shall have a sacrifice for this! They shall! they shall! And, well, the sacrifice is needed, for look at the sores! Look at the sores!"

But the new mother, standing near as if in a trance, saw not the sores. She saw only her Clever Queen, and frantically hugged the child to her breast. You couldn't tell whether she was laughing or crying. Upstairs she took her after the excitement had died down. A big fire was lighted, as all thought of sleeping for many hours was gone. She dared not put the baby alone in the hammock again, so she sat in the hammock herself, and swung to and fro as she cuddled Clever Queen in her arms; and as she swung, she sang:

> "They stole my Pretty Diamond;
> They were horrible and mean.

But I've got another darling,
And her name is Clever Queen.

"Then they stole away my darling;
Who so terrible and mean?
But we cast a spell of magic,
And brought back my Clever Queen."

Again and again she sang her happy song, while Old Grandma sat near the fire, grunting and chuckling to herself. And as she chuckled and smiled, she began to nod; and she nodded and nodded till finally she went to sleep. And as she slept, the singing grew fainter and fainter, and the fire burned lower and lower, till at last they were all asleep—Clever Queen, the mother that bought her, the mother pig and the baby pigs, the puppy dogs, and everybody, all asleep!

CHAPTER **8**

Trying to Heal
the Sores

DURING all the excitement Mr. Rooster had kept
as quiet as could be; but at three o'clock in the
morning he opened his eyes, stretched forth his neck, flapped
his wings, and called out, "Cock-a-doodle-do!" That woke
up Old Grandma, and she began to poke the fire together
again. That woke up Pretty Diamond's mother, and she
began to rock the baby again. That woke up the baby, and
she began to cry. That woke up the mother pig downstairs,
and she began to grunt. That woke up the dogs, and they
began to bark; and in just a few minutes the whole village
was astir for another day, for "early to bed, and early to
rise" is always the rule in the Jungle.

The menfolk sharpened their big knives and talked of
going to work. The womenfolk began to busy themselves
with preparations for cooking the morning rice. While Old
Grandma put on the pot of rice, Pretty Diamond's mother
took down another blanket and, throwing the dirty blanket
in which Clever Queen had been wrapped over near the
waterpot to be washed, was just about to wrap up the little
girl again, when she saw the horrible sores for the first time.

"Grandma! Grandma!" she cried. "Come look at my
babe! Oh, what sores! Oh, what sores! Grandma, what
shall I put on them?"

Old Grandma thought little, but spoke easily: "You know the leaves. Spit on the leaves and stick them on. In a few days the sores will be better; and look out for the fry smell."

The fry smell is the smell of anything frying, and the devil worshipers are very afraid of it. They think it goes into their blood and produces boils and abscesses if they smell it while they have sores or pimples. So while Old Grandma cooked, the mother gathered the leaves, and spat on them, and stuck them all over Clever Queen's body. Whenever she saw anyone beginning to fry the curry, which is a stew that they usually cook to eat with the rice, she covered up the baby's face and hastily went as far away from the place as she could. She did this several times a day for several days—but the sores did not get one bit better.

"Well," said Old Grandma, "I suppose we shall have to have a sacrifice; I promised the devils a sacrifice." So they called the family together, and, sitting down around a roast chicken, they touched hands and prayed the devils to please accept this sacrifice, and let the sores get better. But the sores didn't get one bit better.

"Well," said Old Grandma, "we had better call the witch doctor."

"Yes," said the witch doctor, "this is the result of the curse, and medicine is no good; bring me some oil and I will bewitch it, and then the sores will get better when you rub the oil on them." So they got some oil, and the witch doctor sat down on the ground, and, rubbing his hands, muttered something like this over the oil:

> "The curse is finished, the curse is done;
>   The baby has come, the spirits have gone.
> "The curse is powerful, but magic is strong,
>   The curse must stop before very long;
> "Now heal, now cure, make better, make well.
>   Sores, go away from her quickly, pell-mell. *Pwa!*"

And as he shouted *"Pwa!"* he clapped his hands loudly.
Then he told them to rub the oil on the sores. They rubbed
and they rubbed. But the sores didn't get one bit better.

Then one day there came to the village a man selling
medicine—a Burmese medicine man. Two baskets were
suspended from a bamboo across his shoulder. There were
bottles; there were tins; there were roots; there were leaves;
there were powders; there were pills; and there were horns
and bones.

"Medicine! medicine!" he cried. "Strong medicine! Cures
fry smell, ringworm, headaches, corns, sores, pimples, red
and black children's diseases; sneezing medicine, itching
medicine, fever medicine, weakness medicine, famous rhi-
noceros blood and tiger fat; medicine for all! Medicine!
Strong medicine!"

As he paused for breath, Pretty Diamond's mother drew
near and showed him little Clever Queen's sores. "Is your
medicine able to cure this?" she asked. He laughed at the
idea of any disease being able to withstand his medicine,
and, mixing some bones and tiger fat and whatever-else-I-
don't-know all together, he told them how to apply it, and
said, "Now the cure is absolutely sure, if you keep away
from the fry smell. Don't touch iron, and don't eat anything
sour." So with joy they bought the Burmese man's medicine, and rubbed it on, and followed the instructions— But
the sores didn't get one bit better.

Then one day Old Grandma came back with some star-
tling news. "Daughter, daughter, did you hear? Did you
hear? The God worshipers have a big house and a Sickness
House at the Village of the Palms four miles away."

"But, Grandma, how dared you to go? Have you not
heard that the white God worshipers eat children?" answered Pretty Diamond's mother, as she shuddered at the
very thought of it.

"Aye! So I have heard; but I have also heard that the

white man is a very clever medicine man and has all power over the fry smell. They say that people come five days' journey to eat his medicine, and that everybody walks away cured. I went myself today. Thought I, 'He can't eat me, anyway,' for I had been told that they never tried to eat any but babies. So I went and there I saw him, tall and white. But his hair is black like ours, and his tongue—his tongue, it speaks our words. At first I couldn't hear; there were many people. There were Indians, there were Chinese, there were Burmese, and there were Karens. To the Indians he talked in black words, to the Burmese he talked in Burmese words, to the Karens he talked in our words; and I saw him feel a little baby, and give it some medicine. I nearly shook with fear, but the baby's mother wasn't a bit frightened, and I whispered to her, 'Aren't you afraid he will eat your baby?' And she laughed and he laughed.

" 'Grandma! Grandma!' he said, 'whoever told you that? I eat babies? Come to my house and see my babies.'

"And after a while a lot of us went, and there he had two white babies—one this big, and one smaller than Clever Queen. Oh, how white! As white as flowers of heaven. They were too white to touch, and you could see that they never got sick, and I said, 'Can you cure sores?' and he said, 'Bring the baby here to the Dispensary, and let me see it. Ma Ma will help me, and I think we can cure your little granddaughter.' Daughter! Daughter! Do you hear me talking? He said it! He said it! He can! I am sure he can! We've tried everything. Come on. Daughter! Daughter! Let us take little Clever Queen to the Dispensary for the white God worshiper to heal."

But the poor mother stood there speechless and trembling, her face seemed to be frozen with fear, and all she could do was to clutch her babe closer and closer to her heart.

The devil doctor pushed a bamboo splinter through the holes of the bones. Then turned them about and measured and chanted.

CHAPTER 9

Divining With the Chicken Bones

CLEVER QUEEN'S new Mother trembled with fear for some time, but by and by she found words, and said, "Where did you say the white man's Sickness House is? four miles away at Ohndaw, the Village of Palms?"

"Aye," grunted Old Grandma, "it is not so far; we can go there easily."

"But have you not told me yourself of the terrible curse that rested on that place? I can still remember when I was a girl that you told us stories as we sat around the fire at night, stories of the tribe of Shans that tried to make a village there. You told us of the flood that caused a famine for two years. You told us how they tried to build a pagoda, and how the powerful spirits broke it down three times so that it was never crowned. You told us how it was cursed and how two men who tried to dig up the treasure at the bottom of the pagoda were killed in the attempt. Oh, Grandma—"

"But, Daughter, fear not. That is all past," her mother tried to assure her. "Has not the white man lived there for many years? The spirit he worships must be more powerful than the one that broke down the old pagoda, for we hear no more about people dying there. Indeed, all get better

as soon as they see the big white God worshiper. He is a
powerful medicine man too. Come get little Clever Queen.
We will go."

"But Grandma, I'm afraid."

"Afraid? Afraid of what?"

"Oh, Grandma, you know, the spirits. Maybe the spirits
will get angry with us if we go to the God worshipers' Sickness House, and will smite us all with sores. Oh, oh!"

"Well, can we not again call the devil doctor, and have
him divine with the chicken bones? He can tell us if our
trip will be successful."

"Ah, Grandma, now your words give me strength! Of
course. Why didn't we think of that before? The chicken
bones never fail. Do we not divine with the chicken bones
before we commence our rice planting, and before we go on
a journey, and before we build a house? Yes, of course, let
us call the devil doctor, and we will have him divine with
the chicken bones for us."

Forthwith a chicken was killed and roasted. After being
offered to the devils for a sacrifice, it was eaten. The wings
and the thigh bones of the legs were carefully preserved
and put in a woven bamboo basket. Then the devil doctor
was called.

He was a rough-looking man with disheveled hair. He
came slowly up the bamboo ladder which led into the
house, and sitting cross-legged on a mat placed in the raised
part of the room, waited for Grandma to make known her
request.

"Oh, doctor," she said, coming right to the point, "our
little baby is sick, and covered with sores. The oil, the sacrifice, the medicine, nothing makes her better. Now, there-
fore divine for us with the chicken bones, and tell us where
to go that our little one may be healed."

Now maybe you know, and maybe you don't, but about
halfway from the top to the bottom of the chicken's thigh-

bone there is a tiny little hole. After placing the bones carefully on a bamboo tray before him and after muttering certain secret prayers, the doctor took the finest little splinter of bamboo, and finding the hole in each bone, stuck a part of the tiny splinter into it. He then put them carefully together, and turned them, now this way, now that way, carefully measuring and making incantations as he did so. He then took a piece of charcoal and drew all kinds of lines on the bottom of the bamboo tray, which all looked very mystifying indeed. Finally he turned to Old Grandma, and intoned very solemnly with outstretched hands: "I see footsteps going to the north, but they come not back. I see footsteps going to the east, but they come not back. I see footsteps going to the west, but they come not back. I see footsteps going to the south, and coming back."

A profound silence rested on everybody. Every word was treasured. They waited to see if he would say any more; but that was all. He was paid a whole silver rupee, and departed.

The silence continued for a moment, then the daughter broke it by saying, "Oh, Grandma, what does it mean, what does it mean? Footsteps going to the north, to the east, to the west, but they do not come back?"

"Ah ha, my daughter, what is there hard about words like that? It means that if we take our Clever Queen to the north, or to the east, or to the west, she will not get better, but she will die. It warns us not to go to the north, or the east, or the west."

"Then the footsteps going and coming from the south, what does that mean?"

"Daughter, Daughter, are you so stupid that you cannot understand words so plain? Why, it means that if we take our Clever Queen to the south, we shall bring her back again. It means that she will get better if we go toward the south."

"To the south! That's down the river. To the south; that's
— Why, Mother, to the south, that is toward the old village
of Ohndaw, where the white God worshiper has his Sickness
House."

"Aye, indeed it is!" chuckled Old Grandma; "at once I
knew it. Did I not tell you? We will take our Clever Queen
to the white medicine man. Daughter, how slow you are
to understand! Do you not know by this time that Grandma
is also well acquainted with the ways of the devils? You
heard him say the footsteps were coming back. Fear no
more. There is help and healing with the God worshipers.
Come, Daughter, let us go."

"But Grandma, are you sure it is toward the south?
Then all right, we will go. It must be all right, the chicken
bones never fail."

And early the next morning they bundled up little Clever
Queen and tied her onto her new mother's back. And Old
Grandma and the new mother and Clever Queen made
their slow way toward the Mission Dispensary.

CHAPTER 10

Her First Visit
to the Dispensary

DOWN the trail they went, over little hills and
through a bamboo forest, bowing with their two
hands together as they passed the Pagoda at Kawkeyet, halfway there. On down over three little bridges, till they
could see the tufty tops of the beautiful Ohndaw coconut
palms. "Daughter, we are here!" breathed Old Grandma.

"What shall we do? What shall we say?" sighed the
fearful mother.

"Nay, be not afraid. He will speak first; our words will
be easy," replied Old Grandma. "Be not troubled for your
words."

They came closer. "There, there it is! The Sickness
House! Look at the people!" she added. And, forgetting her
fear, the mother in wonder and surprise saw Indians, Burmese, Chinese, and Karens—all there. They came closer and
took their place with the waiting crowd on the veranda.

What a crowd it was! Sore eyes, boils, and ulcers; ringworm, itch, and toothache; fever, worms, and dropsy;
grandpas, youths, and maidens; uncles, aunties, nieces. But
the poor frightened mother had seen all these before; her
nervous eyes still wandered around over the crowd, for she
was looking for the big white God worshiper, whom the
people all called Thra. As she looked, a door opened, and

41

there he was! So tall, so white, in a long coat so white, and
by his side there came an old man whose face was one
huge grin. "It's all finished!" he said, opening his mouth for
everyone to see, and added as he propped his mouth wider
open, "It didn't hurt a bit!"

"Next!" called Thra, and the door closed again.

The grinning Grandpa was the center of attraction.
Everybody had a look at where the aching tooth used to be,
and everybody smiled his approval and added, "Oh yes, he
is a powerful medicine man."

The door opened again and a girl came out with eye
drops still showing on her face. "They are better already!"
she said, and in turn, becoming the center of attraction,
added, "There are two kinds of eye medicine: White-eye and
red-eye medicine."

"Do you think he can find a medicine for our baby's
sores?" asked Clever Queen's new mother timidly.

"Sores! Humph! Sure, he has the best sore medicine!
Look here, do you see this? See that picture of the rabbit
on these eye drops. That's why it is good medicine. Don't
you know how our elders have always said that the rabbit
was the wisest doctor and the wisest lawyer. This Thra
says that in his language his name means the same as
'rabbit,' so he puts that rabbit picture on his medicine. So
isn't it the best medicine?"

All these words made a profound impression on the timid
mother. Her fear was almost forgotten. She felt very happy.
But when at last the door opened, and Thra called, "Next!"
—and they were next—she just managed to move into the
room with Old Grandma and the baby, and then became
speechless.

The room was so white, and it smelled of medicine, and
there were glass bottles with medicine in them, and a little
glass house with all kinds of queer-looking shining things in
it. It was no use trying, she couldn't talk. But the strange

part of it all was, Thra didn't seem to mind whether she talked or not, but smiling at Old Grandma, said, "Well, Grandma, is this the baby?" And turning to Tha E Sein, a nice clean Karen nurse, he said, "Better run over to the house and call Ma Ma; she's better with the babies than I am."

In a few minutes the white God-worshiping Ma Ma came. She was whiter even than Thra, and she smiled so sweetly that the confidence of the Jungle women was completely won; and before they could realize it Ma Ma had the little baby in her lap, and was unwrapping it.

(Of course by this time you have guessed that the tall white God worshiper was I. That is quite right; and the white God-worshiping Ma Ma was Mrs. Hare.)

"Oh, the poor little thing!" I heard her say, and, turning around, I saw one of the most pitiful sights I have ever seen in my life. Yes, it had sores—running sores all over it, and that was bad enough; but it certainly had not had a bath since the sores had started, and it is impossible to say for how long before that, and the dirty condition of that little baby was indescribable.

"Have you any hot water, Thra?" asked Ma Ma. "Tha E Sein, get the basin; we'll have to give the baby a bath before we can do anything." The basin was brought, and with the steaming kettle in my hand I was just about to pour out some hot water when there was a terrifying scream from the frightened mother.

"Oh, what are you going to do?" she said. "Are you going to cook her?"

We didn't try to keep back our amusement, but laughed right out. "No, no, auntie," we said; "we're not going to cook her, we are going to bathe her."

"*Bathe* her?" echoed the frightened woman. "But Thra, she is sick! She has sores! She will die if she touches water! Oh, Thra!" Even Old Grandma was on the verge of panic; but she remembered suddenly that the chicken bones had said, "Go to the south"; and she was able to control herself.

Now all this time Clever Queen had looked on un-
concerned, but the whiteness of everything and her mother's
fear now produced similar results in her, and I want to
draw the curtain over the next horrible half hour. Let me
only say that at the end of that time Clever Queen, with
clean bandages and a clean cloth around her, sat, soothed,
happy, and contented, on the lap of her smiling delighted
mother. Old Grandma was saying over again and again,
"Surely we'll come again tomorrow," and Thra and Ma Ma
were wiping off the perspiration caused by one of the most
strenuous half hours in their lives.

To the curious and friendly crowd outside, the mother
said, for talking was strangely easy now, "Aren't their ways
so different from our ways? Who ever heard of bathing a
sick baby! I thought they were going to cook her."

The crowd laughed. "Ha, ha! we don't get surprised at
anything they do anymore. You see, in a few days your
baby will be better."

"Surely it will! The chicken bones said to come to the
south," said the mother, "so we know she will get better.
We know she will get better. In fact, she's better already;"
And she hugged her dear babe close to her breast.

Help and Healing With the God Worshipers

Down the stairs they went, and out the front gate; then, pausing and turning around while she walked a few steps backward, the mother called softly:

"Come on, Kalar, come on!
We're going back, we're going back.
Come down the steps and through the gate,
Come, come, Kalar, come, come!"

By doing this, she was sure that the baby's spirit would not remain in the Sickness House; and there is no telling what awful thing might happen if the baby's spirit were left behind. But after repeating these words, she felt quite safe and sound, and followed Old Grandma in single file, along the little jungle trail homeward.

The longer they walked, the more they talked; the more they talked, the more excited they became over the whole morning's adventure; so when they reached the village, they soon had an eager crowd around them as they told of the tall white God worshiper, his wife, and the Karen nurse, and all the wonderful things they had seen that day. They told about the grinning grandpa who had his tooth pulled, of the girl who had sore eyes, of the medicine with the rabbit brand on it, and of the funny ways the white people had, ending up with, "Imagine bathing a sick baby!"

The village folks laughed and laughed, and thought that was the queerest thing they had ever heard of; but in the crowd was another old grandma—old and wrinkled. Not a tooth remained in her head, but in her mouth there was a wad of betel nut that she always kept there and rolled round and round, letting the red juice run down the corners of her mouth, making her look rather like a cannibal. Her hair was disheveled, her head was shaky, her voice was squeaky. She had listened intently to all that had been said; but now she made her way into the crowd, and standing right in front of Clever Queen's mother put her finger up in a warning manner and said, "You'd better be careful! You'd better be careful! I tell you those white people are Daw-ta-kars. I know! Haven't I heard people tell all about white people? They're Daw-ta-kars! They're Daw-ta-kars! That's what they are! And some day they'll eat you."

"Oh now, Old Grandma, don't say that," began the mother.

But the old grandma angrily went on, "Don't I know? Haven't I heard? I tell you they are Daw-ta-kars, and some day they'll eat you."

"But, Old Grandma, they were as kind as kind could be; they—"

"Huh! Of course! Don't we put salt near the animal traps? Don't we sprinkle rice near the bird traps? Don't we put bait on the fishhooks? Can't I remember hearing those that told, that they saw someone who said, that someone told them, that once there was a white man, and he gathered up a lot of young folks, and for a time it looked as if he were kind and good; then he put them on a boat one day, and took them across the ocean and fed them to the Daw-ta-kars. An' we've never seen or heard tell of 'em ever since! Huh, you can't tell me! But what do I care? If you want to get eaten, then go to the white Daw-ta-kar, go every day! Eat his medicine, eat! And some day he'll take you, and drag you down under the water! But don't ever say I never told you. I've surely told you.

"Yes, and if you don't believe me, you go into his house some day, and you'll see a little box in one corner, and it's just jammed full of devils and spirits of the people that he has eaten; and he can make them sing, or play the band, or laugh, or do anything he wants them to do. But what's the good of talking to this young generation? You want to get eaten, well, then go, go, go to your white Daw-ta-kar; but don't say I haven't told you!"

The old grandma looked around on the crowd, and seeing fear on every face, was well satisfied with her speech. Having spoken, she hobbled away muttering to herself, "Let them go to the Daw-ta-kar! Of course they'll go, but I've told them, anyway."

The poor mother's joy was gone. Was this indeed a trap the white God worshiper was laying to catch her and her little Clever Queen? "Oh, Grandma," she said, "what shall I do? What shall I do? But the chicken bones never fail. We will go again tomorrow. We will go! We've tried everything else; if we stay here our baby will die, and we will surely keep our eyes open as we go, to see if what Old Grandma says is true."

So the next day they went to the Dispensary again. They were not nearly so frightened this time; the Ma Ma was there and bathed the baby and put on nice ointment. And they went again the next day, and the next. Clever Queen was getting well so quickly, and how she enjoyed her bath! The only time she cried was when she was taken out of her tub. But the sores—they were drying up and healing quickly; even if those people were Daw-ta-kars, as the old grandma declared, there was indeed help and healing with the God worshipers.

And every day as they came home they gave the news of the day's happenings at the Dispensary. They told of the sick people helped, and of the kind words spoken; and every day others in the village, hearing the wonderful things they told, joined the little group that went down the jungle trail toward the Mission Station. The things that paralyzed with fear the first day soon became commonplace; but each day revealed some new kind of wonder.

Clever Queen's mother became so fearless that one day she followed the nurse to get water; the next moment I heard a shout, *"Ah-m-lay!"* which is a Burmese exclamation meaning "Oh, Mother!" and running to the room where the sink was, I found her transfixed in front of the faucet.

"Where did the water come from?" she gasped, "and where has it gone?"

The Karen nurse was speechless with laughter, and though we explained and pointed to the water tank over the well, she was very quiet during the rest of the treatment. I wonder what she told the village folks when she returned that day.

CHAPTER 12

In the House of the God Worshiper

"MOTHER," said Clever Queen's new mother one day as they were going home through the jungle, "next day let us go to the white man's house. You said you saw his babies. I, too, want to see them. I'm not afraid anymore. They can speak our words. Will he let us go into his house?"

"Aye, surely he will!" answered Old Grandma. "I like to go into his house myself. Ma Ma, she cooks all kinds of bread; and sometimes she lets us taste. Many times I have gone. Tomorrow we shall go again."

So the next day they started out a little earlier than usual, and arrived at the Dispensary before Thra had come. "Good!" said Old Grandma, "we shall go at once to his house, and maybe we shall see him eating; he eats with his wife and his children at the same time, not like us; and they sit on big, tall chairs, at a table with high legs. It is all very wonderful."

They quickened their steps, and, arriving at the Mission Bungalow, went slowly and timidly upstairs. Sure enough, my family and I were at breakfast. So, very quietly they entered, and sat on the floor in the doorway of the dining room.

"Ho, Grandma," I said, as soon as I saw them, "have you eaten your rice?"

"All finished," she replied.

"You've come early today, Grandma," I said.

"Yes, Thra. Clever Queen's mother said she would like to see your babies; and we've brought you a little present."

She arose, and from her basket produced five duck eggs.

"Thank you so much, Grandma," I said; and seeing that we were pleased with her gift, Grandma smiled all over. You can imagine how people smile all over, can't you; well, that's the way Grandma smiled. And then we chatted about Clever Queen and how happy we were living up there in the Jungle among such kind people, and soon our breakfast was all over.

"Come sit in the front room, Grandma," I said. "You know we are God worshipers, and we have a custom to pray to God every day. Wouldn't you like to see how we do it, and listen to what we tell Him?"

We all moved into the front room. Ma Ma had little Lenny on her knee, Eileen sat near me, and we had the Morning Watch text for the day. Next we took a few questions in the Sabbath School lesson, and then we got down on our knees to pray. Grandma didn't know what was going to happen, and began to go out, but I said, "Don't go, Grandma, this is the way we talk with God. You listen; God can talk and understand Jungle words too, and I'll talk to Him in Jungle words today, so that you can understand." Then we prayed.

You know the way all Christians pray; and in our prayer we prayed for the people in the Jungle, and for the poor little sick babies that came day by day, and we prayed that God would make them all better for Jesus' sake, Amen.

"Are you finished?" asked Grandma, as we got up from our knees.

"Yes," I said, "could you understand what we said?"

"Understand? Why, they are our words. But where is your God? We couldn't see Him. Could He hear you?"

And, of course, you can imagine what a lovely time we had visiting with Old Grandma and telling her about our great, big, powerful God.

Then it was time to go to the Dispensary, so I went out of the room onto the back veranda. Ma Ma had gone to the kitchen for something, and Eileen ran to the bedroom and brought out her doll. As Eileen came out with her doll, Old Grandma and Clever Queen's mother must have thought it was another little baby. They watched Eileen dress it; and then Eileen must have dropped it, for by the time I was just leaving the foot of the stairs, a terrifying scream came from the dining room, and the next minute Clever Queen's mother came rushing out to the kitchen.

"She's killed it! She's killed it!" she screamed.

Ma Ma ran inside, and finding everything all right, said, "Eileen, what is the woman screaming about?"

"I don't know," said Eileen; but by this time we all knew, for both Old Grandma and the mother were staring petrified at Eileen's doll. "It's killed! it's killed!" she said.

We all laughed, and tried to explain that it was only a doll and wasn't really alive, and that it could fall down without being hurt very much. And we tried to give them the doll to examine; but they pulled away, and it was a long time before either of them would dare to touch it.

And every now and then during the treatment that day Old Grandma would say, "Clever! The cleverness of these white people! Did you ever hear tell of such a thing? A made baby so white and pretty! If it could only eat now, it surely would be real.

"Huh, wasn't I frightened!" she went on. "I thought it might be someone's spirit, or—or—" then getting very quiet and almost breathing the words, she whispered, "Thra, have you ever seen a Daw-ta-kar?"

"A Daw-ta-kar?" said I. "Why, Grandma, there are no such things. That is only what people say to frighten you."

"But, Thra," she said, "some people say *you* are a Daw-ta-kar. Would you eat us?"

But when she saw the Karen nurse laughing, and when I further assured her that it was only people talking to make others frightened, and that we had never eaten any-one and never would, she felt quite a little better. But she quickly added, "Thra, they say that you have a box jammed full of devils and spirits in your house, and you can make them talk and sing just whenever you want. Thra, have you?"

For a moment I looked truly puzzled; and then as the solution of her fears dawned upon me, I just had to hold my sides with laughter.

"Come tomorrow again early, Grandma," said I, "and I'll show you the little box; but don't be frightened, there are no devils in it."

What do you think the little box was?

CHAPTER 13

The Singing Box

"**W**ELL, Grandma, you've come," I said, as I saw her coming quietly upstairs.

"We've come," she grunted, with a big smile on her face.

"And how's Clever Queen this morning?" I asked.

"All better, Thra," said Grandma, as she pushed the mother forward to show us.

The sores were indeed healing very quickly, and Old Grandma was delighted when I said, "Oh, isn't that fine! Grandma, I think I can give you the medicine now, and let you do it at home; then you won't have to come to the Dispensary every day. Do you think you can put the medicine on all right?"

"Yes, and we'll bathe her every day too. We're not afraid to bathe her anymore when she has sores," she answered; and then remembering that they had come early to see the strange little box, she added, "Thra, you remember you said that you'd show us the—"

"Surely, so I did, Grandma!" I answered. "Come on into the front room. Now first let me open it, and show you all that there is in it."

Of course you have guessed by this time that it was our phonograph; but you must remember that Grandma had never seen or heard a phonograph before. So I opened it, and showed her the pile of records. "Now, Grandma, you feel one of these," I said. "That doesn't look like a devil,

As the record played, Grandma held on to her sides, and laughed and cried, until at last she called out, "Enough! It will kill me!"

now, does it? You see it is just a round piece of hard, flat rubber. See, here are some more!" And I let them both feel and handle them, till they smiled at the very idea of being afraid of things like that.

"Huh!" grunted Old Grandma, "fancy anyone's being afraid. Of course, if it looked like a baby now, then we might be afraid," she added quickly, remembering suddenly the experience with Eileen's doll the day before.

Then I showed her the works, and the spring, and the turntable going round and round. "You see, Grandma, there are no devils or spirits at all," I said. Then I tried to explain vibration and how sound was produced. But although Grandma looked wise, I was quite sure she began to doubt all I had said when I explained that the record could reproduce those vibrations and make sound.

"Now," I said, "this record was made while people were singing, so it must sing." I put the record in position, dropped the needle gently onto the record, and it began to sing. Poor Grandma! Speech was impossible! Her face paled, her knees shook, she clutched frantically at Clever Queen's mother, and began to retreat.

"Oh, now don't be frightened, Grandma!" I said, "it won't hurt you. Now listen, here is a band playing."

Standing was at last impossible, but they had learned to believe us enough not to run away, as very many people had done when they heard the phonograph for the first time, so they just sat down, at a good distance, however, and as near to the door as they could be.

"And now, Grandma, here is one you will enjoy; it is a visit to a farmyard, and you'll hear the ducks and the pigs and the dogs," I said, as I put on another record. And you should have seen Grandma! As the beautiful music brought in the ducks quacking, the pigs grunting, and the dogs barking, she began to feel herself, and I said, "Grandma, what's the matter?"

She said, "I don't know if it is real, or if I'm dreaming!
Is it true?" She looked so puzzled, and at last began to
laugh. "Oh," she said, "he must be telling the truth, although
I can't understand it a bit. But listen, there's a dog, and
Daw-ta-kars don't eat dogs. No, Daw-ta-kars don't eat dogs.
What he says must be true! Ho, indeed, the wisdom of the
white man! Who ever heard tell of such things!"

"Now, Grandma, how do you like that?" I asked. "Now
you're not afraid of it anymore, are you? Listen, here is one
singing your words." And I put on a Karen record.

That convinced Old Grandma. "Oh," she said, "that's
the way the children sing in school! So it is! So it is!"

"Here's one to make you laugh, Grandma," I said, and I
put on a laughing record. Oh, dear me, what fun we had!
There was no more sitting down. Grandma got up and
turned round and round, and laughed and laughed till she
cried. "Oh, Thra!" she said; "oh the wisdom of the white
men!" But she couldn't talk anymore. As the record laughed
and roared, Grandma held onto her sides, and laughed and
cried, till at last she called out, "Thra, enough! enough! It
will kill me! enough! enough!"

"Huh!" at last she grunted. "The ignorance of that
woman who said it was devils! Huh! I'll tell them! I'll tell
them! And I'll bring her to see for herself."

She kept her word. Grandma was always a frequent
visitor at the Mission House, and she always came with a
company who wanted to hear the magical singing box, as
they always called it.

"Here's the medicine, Grandma," I said, after the treatment that day. "Rub it on the sores after the bath each
morning."

"Is it the same medicine that you put on each day?"
asked the mother.

"Surely," I said, but she looked unconvinced. She looked
at it, and smelled it, then handed it back.

"It hasn't the rabbit picture on it, Thra. Please put a rabbit picture on it."

At once I saw the point and pasted on one of the Dispensary rabbit-brand labels; and, smiling, they went away, promising to be back again next week.

Of course, you know there are thousands of people in towns and cities of Burma who ride on streetcars, talk through telephones, use cameras and phonographs, and understand everything the white men have and do; but this is the way the poor ignorant devil worshipers from the Jungle always act when they first get acquainted with white people.

CHAPTER **14**

The Spirit Trap

DOWN the steps and through the gate they went; but they were hardly out of sight when Old Grandma stopped, and turning around to her daughter, who had Clever Queen tied on her back, she said: "Did you ever hear tell of such wonders! Did you hear the dog? Did you hear the duck? And the laughing!" And at the remembrance of it all Old Grandma had to sit down, while she laughed and laughed, and held her sides till she cried. "Oh, I tell you truly," she went on, "if it hadn't stopped, it would have killed me. Ah-ha, we'll tell 'em! The ignorant old woman saying it was devils! Huh! We'll tell 'em!"

All the rest of the way home they repeated and remembered the wonderful things that the singing box did. And by the time they reached the village, they were both laughing so hard that a crowd gathered at once.

"What's all the laughing about?" they demanded.

"Oh, you should have seen it!"

"Seen what?"

"Why, the singing box, of course. Haven't you ever heard of the white man's singing box?"

"Singing box! Whatever do you call—"

It is surprising that the two women could have forgotten their own ignorance and fear so quickly, but they evidently had, for they replied, "Huh! such ignorance! You don't even know what a singing box is! He can make it sing and laugh

58

and talk our words," and at the very thought of the laughing, Grandma went off into another spell.

It was all very amusing, and as the crowd became bigger and bigger, while Clever Queen's new mother and grandma enlarged on the wonders of the white man's singing box, into the crowd came the old grandma who believed it was all devils and spirits that the Daw-ta-kar had eaten. She listened a moment, and then raised a warning finger. "I tell you, you had better look out! you'd better look out! I tell you they are devils and spirits singing and laughing!"

"When did you see it, Grandma?" someone asked.

"I haven't ever seen it, and I don't intend to; but don't I know better than you? Am I not older than you? What do you know? Huh! Looks to me as if you are under the influence of the white man already; you go down there every day. I tell you you'll be eaten up one of these days."

"But, Grandma, they are not devils; we saw inside, we felt—"

"Who dares to contradict me!" growled the old one; "where's the respect for the elders these days? Don't I know? Haven't I heard?"

"But Grandma, they are round flat pieces of hard rubber that make those sounds," Clever Queen's mother tried to explain again.

"They are round flat devils, I tell you!" returned Old Grandma angrily. "I tell you I know! I know! And some day you'll get eaten up. That's what's going to happen to you! Then he'll make *you* into a round flat thing, and make *you* sing. Look out for the Daw-ta-kars!"

She turned as if to go; then suddenly remembering something else she had heard, she turned to the now quiet and serious crowd and continued her speech. "Yes, and the white man's got a spirit trap! He goes around catching people's spirits. Don't I know? Haven't I heard? And haven't I seen him?

"But he didn't catch mine, I tell you! No, indeed, he'll never catch mine!

"Didn't I see him with my very own eyes, standing up in front of some people, and he had a little black box with a wicked-looking eye on the front of it? It was a Daw-ta-kar's eye, it was! And he says, 'Now be still,' and that eye went click, and shut their spirits up inside. Yes, you ought to look scared! I tell you I know. And he takes those spirits out and puts them on flat bits of paper, and sticks them in books. Yes, and all their arms and legs! He's got hundreds of them. But he hasn't got mine! No, indeed! And the poor ignorant children that he has in his school, when they come under his influence, they don't even know what he's up to. They think it's just drawing a picture, and they like it. But I tell you, he doesn't draw anybody's picture. I've seen him. He catches their spirits, that's what he does!

"Oh, how easily you poor creatures are drawn into his net! First you eat his medicine, and then all the rest is easy. But what do I care? Go on! Keep going to your Daw-ta-kar! Go and listen to his singing box! Go! Stand in front of his spirit trap! Stand! But I tell you, some day he'll turn on you and drag you down to the river, and pull you under the water and eat you! Yes, *eat* you! Then he'll make your spirit into a round flat thing and put it into his devil box. Huh!"

The old lady had no more words with which to utter her disgust, and turning on her heels, hobbled away, muttering to herself. "Go! Go! Go! What do I care? Go, and be eaten!"

For a moment the crowd remained silent; then a young man said, "When are you going down to the Mission again, Grandma?"

"Oh, next week," she said. "The sores are so much better that we don't have to go every day anymore."

"Well, I'm going with you next time."

"So am I," chimed in a dozen other voices.

"Huh, who's frightened of the old grandma's words? That's the way she talked about the 'fire boat' when it started to come up the river. She said the Daw-ta-kars would take us away to their country if we rode on it; but we've seen it lots of times, and some of us have ridden on the fire boat."

"Yes," said another, "and do you remember how she went on when the Government stretched the 'talking wire' through the jungle?"

"I declare, I'm not frightened of the white man," said another; "and I'm going with you next time, Grandma."

Grandma just beamed. "And let's ask him about the spirit trap," she said. "He won't hurt us, and he'll tell us all about it. I'm not frightened a bit."

"Neither are we," echoed a dozen voices.

The villagers lined up to have their pictures taken and waited till the eye in the picture box went click.

CHAPTER **15**

Getting Their Spirits Caught

NEXT week what a crowd we had!

The time spent in traveling the four miles to the Mission Dispensary passed quickly as they told and retold the wonderful things that the singing box could do, and they were soon sitting with the others on the veranda, waiting their turn.

"Nephew," said Old Grandma to a young man who sat nearby, "where do you come from?"

"Down there," he answered, giving his hand a wave toward the south.

"What did you come for?" continued Old Grandma.

"I have a terrible sore on my hand," he answered, producing his other hand all wrapped in bandages. "It was so bad I couldn't sleep for days. I was afraid to come at first because I heard that Thra would cut it; but I couldn't get any relief, so I had to come."

"And did Thra really cut it?" ased Grandma sympathetically.

"I'll say he did!"

"And did it hurt?"

"It surely did hurt!"

"Well, why did you let him?"

"Huh, listen to the words of the ignorant! Let him? I

begged him to cut it. But you see this Thra is different. When *he* cuts you, it's only the knife that's sharp. His words are kind, and his hands are gentle, and though it hurts, yet it doesn't hurt, and when it's finished— Sleep? I slept all afternoon and all night."

"Are you afraid of the white Thra, nephew?" continued Grandma.

"I afraid of Thra? Why, whoever is afraid of Thra?"

"Yes, but have you seen his singing box?"

"Huh, singing box! Why, I have gone to the city several times; and in the city nearly everybody has a singing box. They talk and sing in Burmese and in Indian. Singing boxes are common!"

"How wonderful it must be to travel," said Old Grandma. "You've been all the way to the city! They say it would take us five days to walk to the city."

"Yes, but you ride on the fire boat, and get there in one day."

"In one day!" echoed Grandma. "Oh, that's why you are not afraid of anything; you've been all over the world." Here indeed was someone who would know! So Grandma thought she would ask him about the spirit trap. Lowering her voice to almost a whisper, she motioned for her twelve friends who were listening intently to every word of this enlightening conversation to take particular notice, and then, looking as wise as possible, said, "Nephew, have you ever seen the white man's spirit trap?"

"Spirit trap?" he asked, looking puzzled.

"Yes, spirit trap."

"Spirit—"

"They say it's like a little black box with a wicked eye."

"Box—wicked eye?"

"Yes, and they say the white man catches people's spirits in it, with eyes and mouths, and arms and legs."

"Arms and legs!"

"Yes, and they say he tells the people to keep quiet, and the little eye goes click."

"Click?" Then suddenly it dawned on the young man what Grandma was talking about, and instead of looking puzzled he just put his head back and roared.

As I was ready for the next patient, I opened the door.

"Well, now," I said, "everybody seems happy this morning. Hello! Hello! Here's Grandma and Clever Queen. What's all the fun about?"

Even Grandma was laughing; but she was not so badly affected that she could not speak, and hastened to explain: "Thra, they say you have a spirit trap, a little black box with a wicked eye—"

The young man, eager to show his learning and wisdom, controlled himself suddenly and broke in, "Thra, they're talking about a camera; a picture box, Grandma, not a spirit trap."

I quickly took in the whole situation, joined pleasantly in the laugh, and said, "Grandma, wait till after the treatments, and I'll show you the spirit trap. But don't worry, it won't hurt you. It is indeed what the young man says, only a picture box. Now let me have a look at Clever Queen. Sure enough, the sores are almost well. Here, Tha E Sein," I said, speaking to the nurse, "you may treat this case this morning, and give Grandma some more medicine, while I look at this poor boy's hand; then, after that, we'll look at the spirit trap."

The treatments were soon over; and, to their great satisfaction, I brought out the camera. They looked through the ground glass at the back, and what fun they had watching the pictures walking upside down. Then we brought out our photo albums and showed them the pictures of our fathers and mothers and the boys and girls in school, and their delight was unbounded.

"Huh!" grunted one. "That old grandma in the village

calls these spirits; why, these can't move or go. Anybody can tell these are not spirits. Spirits can move and go."

"Yes, but it's no use telling her," added another. "She knows everything. She knows everything!"

"Thra, how much does it cost to make our pictures in the picture box?"

"Well," I said, "I'll tell you what I'll do. I'll just take a picture of you all right now, just so you can understand, and I won't charge you anything."

"Take our pictures?" chorused a dozen delighted people. "Oh, isn't that lovely! Where, Thra? When, Thra? Now?" And you can imagine all the fun they had during that half hour.

At last the little eye went click, and I said, "All finished." At once they crowded round and said, "Quick, Thra, let's see. Let us see." And they were quite disappointed when I told them that there was nothing to see yet. But it would take time to make the pictures with medicine. However, when at last I promised to have the picture ready for them to see next week when they came, they left the Dispensary at once, showing by their actions that they were going to try to make the intervening week go by as quickly as possible.

CHAPTER 16

Providing Food for the Daw-ta-kars

"**I**SN'T it seven days yet, Grandma?" asked a young man as he passed early one morning.

"Huh, seven days! Can't you count?" said Old Grandma. "There are two days more; today is only five days."

"And then are you going?"

"Going? Of course, we're going! Didn't Thra say to come back next week; and doesn't he mean what he says? Doesn't he tell the truth?"

"Yes, but this week has gone so slowly."

"But two days more won't take long—only all day today and all day tomorrow, and then the next morning we go." And in delight the boy skipped off to work, slashing the tips of some bushes with his long sharp knife as he passed.

The two days wore slowly away, and early the next morning a more excited crowd you never saw in all your life. "I wonder what we'll look like?" said one of the girls. "Like white people, or like Jungle people?"

"Like Jungle people, of course!" answered another.

"Yes, but those pictures he showed us last week—lots of them were like white people."

"Well, maybe they were white people."

"Oh, if you're white, does the picture make you white? and if you're Karen, does the picture make you Karen?"

"What are you asking me for? Did I take your picture!"

"Oh, I can't wait, let's run!"

"Yes, hurry up a bit, let's run!"

So the little company, with Clever Queen tied to the back of her new mother, quickened their steps till they were fairly running as they reached the Mission Station. They had started so early, and had run so fast that it wasn't even breakfast time when they arrived, and the school children were still at work in the gardens, in the rice mill, in the kitchen, and in the houses.

"Where's Thra?" they asked a boy who was sweeping up the leaves off the path.

"Right over there near the saw pit, where the boys are sawing timber for our new schoolhouse," he said, and pointed across the field.

"Well, Grandma, here we all are!" I greeted them cordially. "Have you finished your rice so early this morning?"

"Y——es," some said hesitatingly, hastily adding, "We wanted to see our pictures so much that we weren't hungry."

"Well, come along and we'll see that picture!" I replied, and before long twelve or more persons were eagerly crowding around the little piece of paper, all trying to see it and hold it at the same time.

"Oh, look at Grandma!" said the one who was holding it at the time.

"Where? Where?" chorused a dozen voices. "Let me see!" And while the first one put her head back to laugh, the picture passed on to someone else.

"Oh, look at Miss Quick, and her crooked mouth!" squealed another. "Where! Where! Where!" chorused the others, and the picture was taken from her.

"Oh, do I look like that?" said the next. "Look at that old bamboo pipe!"

"Where? Where? Where?" chorused the others, and so they went on, and long after breakfast, after the school had gone in, and while the Dispensary patients were being attended to, they looked and laughed, and laughed and looked at the funniest thing they had ever seen in all their lives.

"But, Thra, we're not pretty like the other pictures you showed us last week," they complained at last.

"Well now, of course you can't blame me for that," I said. "The picture box takes the picture exactly as you are; and if you had a dirty old pipe in your mouth and betel juice dripping down your chin, you can't expect to be as pretty as my school children."

"Surely, that's it!" said one. "The children here don't smoke and don't chew betel nut."

"Yes, and they comb their hair better than we do, and they wash their clothes too; and that makes them pretty."

"Thra, if we didn't smoke and chew betel nut, and if we washed our clothes, would we be pretty too?" some of them asked; and a few of the younger ones said, "Well, we are going to see; we are not going to smoke or chew anymore, and we'll see if we get pretty."

"Just look at my little Clever Queen," said the proud mother who by this time had had plenty of opportunity to gaze at the picture. "Clever Queen doesn't smoke or chew, and she's the prettiest one of the lot of us." A dozen voices said, "Where?" A dozen hands reached to take the photograph to examine Clever Queen's picture.

"So she is!" they all assented at last. "Clever Queen's the prettiest one of the bunch!" Her mother hugged her tight, and Old Grandma added:

"Thra, when Clever Queen grows up, may we send her here to school?"

"Surely you may, Grandma," I said. Then, as if asking Clever Queen's permission, she proudly rubbed the baby's cheeks and said, "Clever Queen, when you grow up, do you want to come here to school and learn all the wisdom of the white man? Do you, Clever Queen?" And Clever Queen just beamed the biggest smile you could ever wish to see.

"Oh, look, she's smiling!" echoed the dozen voices. "She wants to come! She wants to come! She's not frightened by the white man. She's eaten his medicine; her sores are better. She's had her picture taken. Of course she'll go to school when she grows up. And as the old grandma back home would say, 'She'll become food for the Daw-ta-kars.' "

"When do we have to come again, Thra?" said Grandma, as they were leaving.

"Oh, come any time you like," I said. "Clever Queen is all right now. By the time you finish the medicine we have given you, the last little sore will all be healed."

Grandma was proud and happy. "There," she said, "the chicken bones were true! The chicken bones were true! They said footsteps coming to the south were returning to the village; and here we all are returning, and the sores are all healed. Truly there is help and healing with the God worshipers. We'll be back someday, Thra; we'll be back! And when Clever Queen grows up we will bring her here to school, and," laughing outright as she said it, "we'll let the Daw-ta-kars eat her."

And as I watched them returning happily to their village, I wondered if ever little Clever Queen would come to school when she grew up.

But I have something very disappointing to tell you. You will be sorry to hear that Clever Queen's real mother disappeared about this time, and we did not hear of her anymore. She became so afraid of the curse, which she thought had forced her to bring back her baby to the woman who had bought her, that I suppose she thought she had better go somewhere else to live. So we do not know what happened to her, and she does not come into this story anymore. So from now on, we shall call the woman who bought her "Clever Queen's mother," not her "new mother."

CHAPTER 17

Clever Queen
Arrives at School

WELL, Clever Queen grew and grew, and grew and grew, and got bigger and bigger, and fatter and fatter, and taller and taller, till at last she was seven years old. And then one day her grandma said: "Come on, Clever Queen, I've bought you a new dress; I've bought you a slate. I hear that the school has begun for the new year over at the Mission. We want to be proud of you someday, so we are going to send you to school."

Clever Queen was as glad as she could be. She wasn't frightened, as many other little boys and girls have been. Her mother and her grandma had talked and talked about sending her to school when she grew up, till she was quite happy and anxious to go. She put her little bag with the slate in it over her shoulder, and led the little procession through the jungle, down to the Mission School.

On her mother's head was a little box, in which were a comb, a small piece of sandlewood bark, two little dresses, and an extra slate pencil. Old Grandma carried a mat in which was rolled a home-woven cotton blanket and a pillow. This was the sum total of all little Clever Queen's worldly possessions.

Already she had made several visits to the Mission. She knew a few of the children. One big boy came from her very

71

own village; and she had heard the Brass Band before too; but now it was different. This time she was going to school herself. She was going to live there, sleep there, eat there, learn there. She would take her place with the boys and girls in the drill every morning. And the very thought of it quickened her step and made her quite excited. "Come on, Grandma; quickly, Mother!" she said, as she urged them to keep pace with her eager little feet.

But in her mother's heart and in her grandma's heart there were different kinds of thoughts. Their Clever Queen was going to school! It just seemed as if she had grown up all of a sudden, and now they would have one less to cook for, one less sleeping in their little bamboo house; and even if it was only four miles away, it seemed a very, very long way to poor old Grandma just then; for, after all, although they had lived in fear all their lives, right inside their hearts they love and feel lonely just as we do.

But it had to be. They were going to learn to live above this fear and superstition someday. Someday they hoped to be free from the power of the devils; so with smiles on their faces, they called out, "All right, Clever Queen, we're coming!" and hastened their steps.

Down the little hill, across the log bridge, through the— "Listen!" called Clever Queen from her position in front of the line. "Listen!" and through the jungle there came the regular Boom, Boom, Boom, Boom, of the big drum in the Brass Band. "Quickly, Grandma, school has started; the band is playing; the children are doing their drill! Come on, Grandma, quickly!"

The sight of those school children doing their drill each morning is indeed enough to gladden anyone's heart, so the three hastened their steps till they were fairly running; and in a few moments they were standing near the Dispensary watching that wonderful parade.

There was the big tall white man with his band boys.

There were the boys and girls standing in such straight lines, and one of the teachers standing in front as he directed them in their movements.

> "Up, down, up, down, -5-6-7-8.
> In, out, in, out, in, out, 7-8.
> Altogether -3-4-5-6-7-8."

Was there ever anything so beautiful and so lovely, and so pretty, and so wonderful! Such straight lines! All together, at the same time! The exercises stopped. The lines turned toward the school, and as the wonderful music continued, they marched up into school. Left, right, left, right, left, right, left, till they all disappeared. Then the band stopped and went up into school too.

Grandma reached for Clever Queen's hand. She did not know just why it trembled a little, but it did, and, strangely enough, she found it hard to speak. They had stood silent and motionless during the parade, and now school had started, and Clever Queen would have to be put in her class. So together they moved toward the school.

After calling the roll, I was just dismissing the classes to their own rooms as Grandma came onto the steps. "Well, Grandma!" I greeted her; then, noticing the little girl beside her, said, "and who is this you have brought with you today?"

"Why, Thra," she said, "this is Clever Queen; we have brought her to school."

"Clever Queen! Clever Queen! why, so it is!" I said. "I hardly knew her. I haven't seen her for a long time; and she has a new dress on, and her hair is so nicely combed. Why, she looks like a schoolgirl already."

Grandma beamed; so did her mother. "Yes, Thra, we have brought her to school. We like the Mission, and we like the God worshipers. Thra, in our village we are so afraid of everything all the time. We are the slaves of the devils; but we want Clever Queen to be a God worshiper. Teach her anything you like. She's yours, only we'll come to visit her now and then."

"All right, Grandma, all right," I said. "We'll look after Clever Queen. I'm sure she will like it here in school. And you come down just any time you like to visit us."

I took the little girl by the hand and led her gently to the room where the first graders sat around a blackboard, and put her in the care of her teacher. "This is Clever Queen, girls," I said; "be kind to her, and soon she will feel very much at home."

Outside Grandma and Mother lingered till noon; then they turned into the jungle and went quickly home.

CHAPTER 18

School Is Fun for Clever Queen

"**S**O THIS is Clever Queen!" said her teacher.
"Well, she is a nice little girl. Here, Clever Queen, you may sit on the floor over here beside Miss Brave. The next little girl is Clear Gold; the next, Sleep Sweet; that little boy over there is Little Egg, and the next one is Silver Lump."

"Now, children, first and second grades attention!" said the teacher. "This morning we will study a little more about the story of this world. Now answer all together. In how many days did God create this world?"

"Six days."

"That's right. On what day were Adam and Eve created?"

"On the sixth day."

"Fine! Then what did God do on the seventh day?"

"He rested, and blessed it, and sanctified it."

"That's good. Now before very long, while Adam and Eve were happy as they could be, the old devil took the form of a very beautiful snake, and went up into a tree." Clever Queen became suddenly interested. She knew about the devil's becoming a snake, but she did not interrupt; and the teacher continued. "Then he picked a fruit from the tree, and tempted Eve." Clever Queen could not keep quiet any longer. Up went her hand, "Teacher, Teacher," she said, "I know that!"

Clever Queen repeated for her teacher the song she had learned from Grandma about the devil becoming a snake and tempting Eve.

"You do?" asked her teacher.

"Yes, my grandma told me; and when people die they sing that story about the devil."

"Would you like to tell us the words of the song they sing, Clever Queen?"

"Surely," she said, and then repeated:

"God commanded us in the beginning,
  The devil came and destroyed.
God commanded us in the beginning,
  The devil intended to deceive unto death
The woman Eve, and the man Adam;
  The dragon looked, and was not pleased.
The woman Eve, and the man, both of them,
  The dragon looked, and was not pleased.
The great dragon deceived the woman and Adam.
  What was it that he said?
The great dragon took a ripe fruit
  And fed God's son and daughter.
They didn't keep all of God's commands,
  After, they were deceived unto death.
They disobeyed the Word of God;
  God turned His back on them."

"Well, that was good, Clever Queen; who taught you that?"

"Grandma."

"And who told your grandma; has she got it in a book?"

"Why, no, Grandma can't read, and we have no book. I suppose her father told her."

"And who do you suppose told him?"

"Oh, I suppose *his* father must have, because all of us Jungle folk know that song. And Grandma says that's why we have to worship the devils—because God has turned away from us and we have to offer the devils sacrifices all the time so they won't get angry with us."

"Well, Clever Queen, don't you worry about the devils

while you are here at school. They won't hurt you here.
You see, we are trying to obey God here, and He has turned
toward us again, and we can talk to Him and He hears us
and He protects us from the power of the devil."

This was so new and interesting that the little girl just
sat there with her mouth open, taking it all in. Somehow
it felt so good and safe to be in school already.

Then it was time for the next lesson, and the teacher
said, "Now all try to copy these letters that are on the
board, while I start the next class to work, then I'll come
back to you."

Oh, wasn't it wonderful! She was in school. Surely, she
could copy those funny little circles from the blackboard,
and proudly she took her slate and pencil and did the best
she could. To be sure, they were not very pretty, but it
was a start; and, anyway, they were as pretty as Brave's and
Sleep Sweet's. Yes, and Little Egg could not even write
any. Well, it was lots of fun, and presently the teacher
came back and said, "Now, children, you must learn your
letters so you can read. This is the first letter, these two
circles with their mouths open on the bottom we call 'Ka,'
and with all the other marks above it and around it, it
sounds like this: Now you all say it after me. 'Ka Ah Ka'"
and the children chorused, "Ka Ah Ka."

"Ka Erthy Ka," and the children all said, "Ka Erthy Ka."
"Now the next, 'Ka Harthy Ka.'"
"Ka Harthy Ka."
"Next, 'Ka Plercy Ka.'"
"Ka Plercy Ka."
"Ka Arthy Ka."
"Ka Arthy Ka."
"Ka Kaypo Ka."
"Ka Kaypo Ka."

Oh, it was really thrilling! They went over it again,
again, and again, each one taking a turn, till they knew the

exact tone to each of the words. Then after the reading lesson came the numbers, and then recess. It was all so wonderful.

After school in the afternoon Clever Queen joined the little girls who were sent to sweep the girls' house and the Dispensary. The floors didn't seem a bit dirty, and she didn't see the need for all the sweeping; but she was at school now, and she willingly did all she was told.

Then a bell sounded "ding, ding, ding," "ding, ding, ding," and the girls hurriedly put away their brooms and rushed down to the river to bathe. Before she had had half enough fun in the water, the bell sounded again for dinner. With her plate she stood in line, as the girls passed their counter in the cafeteria. She was served with a big heaping plate of rice and a bowl of lentil soup, and with the rest of them sat on her heels and ate with her fingers, for this is the Jungle custom. The rice was good, and the soup was good; but she wanted something else, and looking everywhere without seeing it, at last asked Sleep Sweet, "Where's the rotten fish paste?"

"Oh," laughed Sleep Sweet, "we don't eat that here in school! Rotten fish paste doesn't make good blood; and we want to keep well and strong, so we don't eat it here at school. And we don't smoke or chew betel nut, either."

"No, I don't smoke or chew," said Clever Queen. "My grandma told me never to smoke because I was going to school when I grew up; but fish paste—dear me, I do wish I had some fish paste. But I guess I'll soon get used to it— and I'd rather be here without fish paste than be in my village with all the fear of evil spirits and fish paste."

Clever Queen did soon get used to doing without fish paste; and as the days went by, she just loved her school more and more. It would take too long to tell you everything, so you must just try to imagine how, though at first she was timid, yet, little by little, she learned how to work

her hands up and down and in and out, during the exercises
every morning, and before many weeks she was very much
at home, and felt that she was actually one of the school
children.

"Oh," she used to say to her teacher, who told them
about heaven in their Bible classes, "can heaven be nicer
than school? Can the houses there be any cleaner than
here at school?" And when told that they were, she could
hardly imagine it.

CHAPTER 19

Those Good Friday-night Meetings

A MONG the happiest times she ever had at school were those wonderful Friday-evening meetings when the boys and girls stood up and spoke with God. The first time Clever Queen attended worship on a Friday evening happened to be Blessing Night. One of the teachers told of all the good things God had given them; then one by one the children stood and thanked God for the blessing of food and water, friends and relatives, hands and feet, and, oh, there were so many! Clever Queen did want to stand up and speak too, but it just happened that each one who spoke thanked God for the very thing that she was thankful for, and—but, anyway, her little heart was beating too fast. She couldn't quite take part that Friday evening.

However, not many weeks went by before Clever Queen stood up with the rest of them, and felt the thrill of talking with God.

It was a Praise Night. One of the teachers talked a little while on the subject of praise, and then let the children stand up and repeat "praise" verses. All afternoon Clever Queen had been learning her text, for she knew what was coming. Her teacher helped her find one in Psalms. "O give thanks unto the Lord; for He is good: for His mercy endureth forever." And it was so easy, she could say it well. But when the time came to stand up and say it that evening, her knees shook, her hands trembled, her mouth went dry. She couldn't understand it. Her turn was coming closer and closer. It was nearly down the row to her. Only one more—

"Next, Clever Queen," called the teacher kindly.

And poor Clever Queen forgot every word she had ever learned. She opened her mouth, but nothing came. She broke out in a cold sweat.

"O give thanks," prompted her little mate, Sleep Sweet.

And Clever Queen did her best. "O give—O (cough) O give—O give (cough, cough) thanks. O give thanks. O give (cough) unto the—unto the Lord." She sat down and felt as if the whole world were looking at her.

Surely there was another sentence to her text, but she couldn't say another word. She had been talking to God, and the very thought of it made her tremble. But when her trembling passed away, it left her strangely happy.

Yes, God must have heard. It was just as the teacher said. This happy feeling must be what they call joy and peace. Oh, how different from the terrible fear they had in their heathen villages—and oh, how good it all was!

Then one Friday night the big Thra talked on prayer, and he said that not only can we talk with God, but often He talks with us and He answers our prayers; and then Thra asked if there were any who would like to tell about an answer to prayer, and then—oh, then, that was the best meeting they ever had!

Scented Water stood up and said that once she was going to Rangoon with Ma Ma, and she had her ticket all right; but just before the train started, the ticket collector came to look at the ticket and she couldn't find it; and she looked, and she looked, but it was no good. She couldn't find it. And the ticket man began to get impatient. Then she just turned around and prayed, "O God, help me find my ticket." And right then, almost like a voice, something told her to go and look where she had been buying her rice; so she jumped down out of the train, and ran over to the rice shop, and there was her ticket right on the ground!

Then a boy called Red stood up and said that when he was coming to school, he was waiting at the station for nearly an hour before the train started, and there was such a rush that he wondered how he was going to be able to buy a ticket, so he shut his eyes and prayed, "O God, help me buy my ticket." Just then a man stood up right beside him, and said, "Who wants a ticket? I can't go until to-morrow night," and Red said, "I, I!" and grabbed the ticket and gave the man the money right away.

Then a girl named Serve Rice stood up and said: "I've never even seen a train, but last vacation my mother was going to Lapota, and oh, how I wanted to go! But I was afraid to ask Thra because I hadn't worked off my debt yet, and I was afraid he would say No. So I just prayed, and by and by I saw Thra coming down the path. My heart began to beat fast. I decided that I would ask him; then I was too frightened. When he came up to me he said, 'Well, Serve Rice, so your mother's going to Lapota tomorrow; wouldn't you like to go with her for a few days?' And I said, 'Oh yes,' and didn't have to ask at all."

Then Sharp Diamond—she's the storekeeper—said that one day she lost her key to the cash box. And oh, how troubled she was! She looked and she looked, but she couldn't find it, so she prayed, and a voice said, "Go, and ask Thra;" and though she was very ashamed, she couldn't think of anything else to do, so she went and asked Thra, and he said, "Oh yes, I found it last night when I was closing up," and how happy she was! But she wished she had obeyed that voice sooner.

And there were just lots and lots of other things said

that I have not time to tell you, but Clever Queen was thrilled with a delight that she could hardly explain. It was becoming so simple to her. These were truly God worshipers. They talked with God, and God talked with them, and as she left the meeting that night she said to Clear Gold as they went down the steps, "I'm going to be a God worshiper, aren't you?"

"Surely," said Clear Gold, "and I pray every night; do you?"

"I? Pray? What do you pray every night for?"

"Why, Thra says that if we pray every night and ask God to send an angel to watch over us, no devils or evil spirits can harm us."

"Oh, is that why the God worshipers aren't afraid of the devils? Oh, is that it? Then I'm going to pray every night too." And kneeling just as little Clear Gold taught her to kneel, she shut her eyes and prayed, "O God, dear God, send an angel to look after me too." Then she lay down in peace and slept.

CHAPTER 20

When She Didn't Feel So Good Inside

IN THE Jungle, school opens just at the breaking of the rainy season, during which time we have up to two hundred inches of rain. As you can well imagine, the whole country is in flood for several months. The Salween River rises thirty or forty feet, and as it rushes down toward the ocean, its angry, muddy waters wash away miles and miles of riverbank, and its whirlpools twist and tangle trees and bushes into awful confusion, and make the river very dangerous. As Old Grandma turned to go after bringing Clever Queen down to school for her second year, she lifted a warning finger and said, "Now, granddaughter, don't go swimming in the river when the river's angry"

"All right, Grandma," answered Clever Queen sweetly, and was soon getting ready for school with Sleep Sweet and Clear Gold.

A week passed; the rains settled down heavily. The river rose, and Thra gave the announcement one morning that big tanks put under the eaves of the houses would be used for bathing, as the river was dangerous, and added, "Don't go swimming in the river when the river is angry, or you'll get caught in the whirlpools."

Of course, all the boys and girls said they wouldn't go; but Satan was there, as he usually is whenever boys and girls are trying to do right, and he tried hard to make six little girls disobey. All day long the heavy rain had fallen; but, toward evening, strangely enough, it had stopped, leaving what was left of the day calm and still. The stop-work bell had just rung, and the sweepers, Sleep Sweet, Clear Gold, Clever Queen, Diamond, Brave, and Golden Bead, picked up their spare *longyis* (that's what they call the garments they wear), as they always did, and started off toward the river.

"Oh," said Golden Bead, "I forgot. Thra said not to swim in the river when the river is angry."

"Oh, why can't we? I'm going to anyway," said Sleep Sweet.

"So am I," added Brave; "I'm not frightened."

"Neither am I," said Diamond, and she was the smallest one in the group. "Can't we all swim?"

"Oh well, come on then," agreed Golden Bead; "I don't suppose it will matter for this once."

They hid their *longyis* under their jackets as they passed the school. But, "Hey, where are you little girls going?" demanded a teacher who was there. "Don't you go swimming in the river when the river is angry. If you do, you will be drowned."

"Pooh, we can swim, we aren't frightened!" they answered, and with their little noses up in the air, down the path they went. Down the path, past the house where Diamond's big sister was.

"Here, where are you little girls going? Don't you go swimming in the river when the river is angry," she said.

But the six little girls put their noses a little higher as they retorted, "Pooh, we're not frightened; we can swim!"

And down the path they went, right down to the river.

"Hey, what are you little girls doing down here swimming when the river's angry?" warned a fisherman, who was sitting nearby in a canoe.

"Pooh, we're not frightened!" they said, and with that they jumped in, and swam and dived, and swam and dived, just like little fishes.

It was no use fishing with all that noise nearby, so the fisherman moved off farther upstream, and the girls jumped, and swam, and dived, and chased one another in the water, under the water, faster and faster, and farther and farther, till all of a sudden there was a scream from Diamond, the smallest one in the group. She had dived to escape someone who was chasing her, and had gone too far, and was caught in a whirlpool.

Five girls scrambled out of the water and watched in terror. "Swim, Diamond, swim!" they cried, and Diamond swam. But the cruel whirlpool twisted her away round, and out, farther than ever before.

"Oh, what shall we do? Help! Help!" they cried. "Diamond's caught in a whirlpool! Help!" But the river was making so much noise that no one could hear. Diamond had stopped struggling. Though she was so little, she grimly realized that she must save her strength to keep afloat, and the frantic girls, sick at heart and pale with fear, watched the angry river carry her out and then whirl her around and in toward the shore, out and in, out and in, as she was carried downstream.

"Help! Help! Help!" screamed the poor girls as they followed down the riverbank, but no one heard their cries. "Help! Help! Help!" Then all of a sudden Golden Bead rushed ahead, and stood out on a rock that jutted out a few feet from the bank. She said nothing, but with her eyes fixed on little Diamond, who was floating like a helpless cork on the angry water, she waited, hoping that the current would bring her in, as it passed that point. Closer and closer she came, and nearer and nearer—yes, it was! She was coming in. The other girls saw what was happening, and held their breath. Closer, closer—then a splash! And the next minute Golden Bead had Diamond by the hair and was pulling her out of the current.

"Oh, dear!" said six frightened girls all at once as they sat on the riverbank, and panted. "Oh, whatever you do, don't tell anybody."

"We won't."

"What if Bead hadn't got her. What if—"

"I wish we hadn't come," said Bead.

"So do we," the others chorused.

"I don't feel too good inside," confessed Clever Queen. "Oh, why did we come?" And six little girls hung their heads as they sneaked past the school to their house. And six little girls didn't feel good inside; so they sat very quiet that evening in worship. And six little girls didn't sing the next day as they worked, for it just seemed as if the sun didn't shine for them anymore.

But the next day was Friday, and that night there was another of those Friday-night meetings. Thra was talking on Forgiveness, and six little girls felt that he was talking especially for them when he said, "When we disobey God's commandments, our sin makes us sad, and God knows all about it, for He sees everything, and it makes Him sad. But He has given us a way to make things right; and if we confess our sins, He promises to forgive us our sins, and to forget all about them; then we feel glad again, and God is glad, and all the angels sing and praise God, because they are so happy that we are learning to overcome our sins."

And six little girls felt hungry inside to be happy again. They didn't know just how to confess, but they got their little heads together and decided to tell Thra all about it and ask him to confess for them.

So six little girls waited for me as I came down the

stairs that evening from chapel, and they said, "Thra, who told you all about us?"

"Told what about you?" I asked in surprise.

"About our going swimming when the river was angry!"

"Why I—"

"But you said we didn't feel good inside! And so we don't, Thra; we thought you surely knew all about it." Then they told me all about the terrible adventure, and added, "Oh, Thra, we won't do it again; we've felt so miserable inside ever since."

"Yes, and what if Diamond had been drowned!" added Clear Gold. "It would have been all our fault."

"Well, girls," I said at last, after they had told me all they could think of. "Let's tell Jesus that we are sorry, and then see if He won't make us happy again." So we knelt down and I prayed: "O Lord, forgive these little girls for being disobedient. They have had a terrible lesson. Now please, Lord, make them all happy inside again, for Jesus' sake. Amen."

Clever Queen could hardly wait till the Amen was finished. "I'm happy again, Bead!" she said; "are you?"

"Surely; I feel all glad inside, and so does Diamond. Look at her grinning over there." And as six little happy girls walked off arm in arm, it did seem that even the angels were happy up in heaven.

All day long, boys rowed people across the river to attend the Jungle camp meeting. By nighttime three hundred had come and found places to stay.

CHAPTER **21**

Attending
the Jungle
Camp Meeting

WELL, four more happy years have sped by
before we come to the time of the Jungle camp
meeting, about which I want to tell you now. During this
time Clever Queen grew and grew, till she was a bright,
clean, happy little girl of twelve—and the pride and delight of her mother and grandma.

"You'll be sure to come to the camp meeting next
month, won't you, Grandma," she said one day in the
early new year, as she chanced to see her dear old
grandma at the Dispensary. "Our big Thra has come back
from America, and he has brought a living picture box."

"A living picture box!" puzzled Old Grandma.

"Yes, you know the little picture box; well, it's like that,
only it's different."

"How's it different?"

"Well, you know he can show those pictures at nighttime, on a sheet, and the pictures look like people, but
they are not alive. They are dead pictures. They can't
move or run or laugh, or—"

"Do you mean to say he can show pictures now that
move and run and laugh?"

"To be sure he can, Grandma. I've seen them. And the

people walk. Oh, I never knew before how many white
people there were in the world. And the motor cars run
like beetles. Grandma, I tell you, you must come. And
the Band is going to play the same time that we sing.
And Thra is going to—oh, I don't know what all he is
going to do. But Thra and Peter are talking and talking,
and putting up little pegs of bamboo in the ground, and
they have bought six big cooking pots, and—and—but,
Grandma, you must come, and tell all the others in the
village. Won't you?"

"We'll come, surely," said Grandma; "but we won't tell
the old toothless one about the living pictures that move
and run. She'd surely say they are devils."

"Devils!" said Clever Queen, unable to cover her disgust. "Devils! She thinks everything is devils. Never mind
her. Grandma, you'll come, won't you? I must go; there's
the bell."

As Clever Queen tripped off to classes, Grandma
beamed with pride. "Aye, we'll come; Grandma will
come," she said to herself. Then as her granddaughter
disappeared in the schoolhouse, she turned toward the
jungle and started off toward home.

Did ever a month go by so slowly? Yet each day had
seen wonderful changes in the school grounds. Where
the pegs had been placed in the ground, there now stood
a great big straw chapel—with a place for the Band to
play, and a place for the children to sing, and a place for
Thra to stand, and a sheet for the pictures, and mats in
the schoolrooms for the hundreds of visitors to sleep on,
and plates for them to eat from, and a big row of fireplaces, where they were going to cook. Every day they
practiced and practiced, till everybody could stand at the
same time, and sit at the same time, and sing at the same
time. Surely there had been other camp meetings before,
but this time it was different.

At last the day came. Twice during the night the launch brought up the believers from the outstations down the river. More than a dozen bullock wagons brought in more from the outstations out west, and the boys were rowing people over from across the river all day long, And by that night about three hundred visitors had come and had found places to sleep. People who had never ridden on a boat before, who, before this, had never gone farther than ten miles from their jungle villages, were there. They had come to enjoy the music and the singing; they had come to see the wonderful pictures; and they had come, too, because they were hungry for something better than they had. They were tired of being slaves to the devils, and they were feeling their way to something better.

At half-past five the Band started to play. And at half-past five the crowd started to gather for meeting. Not twenty or thirty as we used to have years ago, but five hundred, six hundred. The straw chapel was well filled, but the crowd still gathered. From nearby villages the bullock wagons were driving in by the scores. There was no more room to sit. Eight hundred, nine hundred. They were standing around; they were sitting up in the nearby mango trees. They pulled bullock wagons up in a row and sat on the tops of them. Over a thousand came to the meeting that night.

What was that? "Sh-sh-sh!" came from hundreds of lips within the chapel, "it's going to start;" and as the great crowd quieted down the big Thra stood up, smilingly spoke words of welcome to the visitors, and then, and then—they started to sing. The Band started to play all together, at the same time. The children were standing up in their places. Their clothes were clean, their hair was nicely combed, their little mouths all opened together, as they sang:

"Let us sing a song that will cheer us by the way,
In a little while we're going home;

For the night will end in the everlasting day,
   In a little while we're going home.
There's a rest beyond, there's relief from every care,
   In a little while we're going home;
And no tears shall fall in that city bright and fair,
   In a little while we're going home."

Thra turned around to the congregation, and said, "Fathers and mothers, and uncles and aunties, don't you want to come too? Try to sing it with us." And you should have heard that Jungle crowd join in with, "In a little while we're going home."

There followed a talk on the nearness of Christ's coming. Then more singing. Then still pictures, showing the increase of knowledge. Then more singing. Then the living pictures, showing the wonders of New York City and a part of the Navy and the Army in action. I cannot take time to tell of the wonder and surprise expressed as the Jungle folks saw the great boats and heard guns shooting—for we had trained the drummer to hit his drum every time the cannons boomed. They had heard about the Great War before, but had no way of imagining what it was like. "Please show it again, Thra," they cried. So, after some more singing and another talk on war's being a sign that Jesus soon would come, the picture of the war was shown again, and the meeting that started at five-thirty in the evening was dismissed at nine-thirty.

As the visitors from the outstations gathered around on their mats in little groups to talk further on the subject, and the near-by visitors harnessed up their bullock wagons and began to move off noisily into the night, Clever Queen said to her little mate as they walked arm in arm to their house, "Clear Gold, I feel strange inside tonight. It surely is going to be only a little while, and then we're going home. But I don't feel quite ready, do you?"

"No, but I do want to go too," said Clear Gold.

"Do you know, I feel that I ought to be baptized. Only I'm not good enough."

"That's just the way I feel," confided Clear Gold. "What would we do if we were tempted and started smoking again?"

"Huh, that's not what I'm frightened by; I have never smoked," answered Clever Queen. "It's keeping the commandments that worries me. I just try and try to obey sometimes; then I forget, and disobey sometimes. And I try and try for all I'm worth not to play on Sabbath, but sometimes I forget. But, Clear Gold, it's only a little while—only a little while, and we'd better be getting ready, don't you think?"

"Yes, indeed, we must surely be getting ready."

CHAPTER **22**

Clever Queen
Is Born Into
the Kingdom

THE meetings continued all the next day, and
every minute was filled with stories and songs
of the glad tidings. The growth of the work in each out-
station was studied, and great was the rejoicing. But it was
the Friday-night meeting that seemed to be the most im-
portant one of all. As it was the beginning of the Sabbath,
everybody was dressed in his best clothes, and the Band
played only hymns. But, oh, such music!

As the crowd gathered into the building, and the boys
and girls took their places on the platform, they all joined
in the opening hymn:

"What a wonderful change in my life has been wrought
    Since Jesus came into my heart!
I have light in my soul for which long I have sought,
    Since Jesus came into my heart.
I shall go there to dwell in that city I know
    Since Jesus came into my heart!
And I'm happy, so happy, as onward I go,
    Since Jesus came into my heart!"

The outstations had been practicing that song during the
year, so most of the visitors could sing it.

As they sat down, Clever Queen's eyes rested on her

grandma and a village girl sitting beside her. The words of the song were still ringing in her ears. Grandma's face was still shining with delight, but the face of the little village girl beside her was sadly thoughtful. She sat there looking at the rows of clean children sitting on the platform; then she tried to snuggle up to Clever Queen's grandma as if she were trying to hide herself. Nervously she tried to tuck as much of her dress out of sight as she could.

Clever Queen wondered at this strange behavior; but soon her eyes were opened, and she knew the reason why. This was the change which they had been singing about. If she had not come to school, that is just the way she would have looked—dress all dirty, hair carelessly combed, mouth red with betel nut, and teeth all blackened with tobacco. There had been a wonderful change indeed; but, as she pondered a moment, she realized it was not all in the clothes or the hair. The little dirty village girl was still a slave of the devils and lived in constant fear and dread; but floods of joy o'er Clever Queen's soul like sea billows had rolled, because Jesus had come into her heart. Yes, Jesus had come into Clever Queen's heart.

But Thra was talking. "If ye love Me, keep My commandments," he read. Clever Queen's thoughts turned suddenly from feeling good about the change that had come into her life, and she paid good attention to what Thra said, because keeping the commandments—that was the very thing that troubled her.

"So many people think they dare not become Christians because they cannot keep all the commandments," he was saying; "but, fathers and mothers, I want you to remember that when the lawyer asked Jesus which was the greatest commandment, He gave an answer that fits you and me and all of us. He said, 'Thou shalt love the Lord thy God with all thy heart, and with all thy soul, and with all thy strength, and with all thy mind; and thy neighbor as thyself.' This shows the justice of the living God. Each one must serve Him with *all* his heart, and *all* his strength. And God requires of those who have much light more than He requires of those who have little; yet it is the one just standard. He demands *all* of *your* heart and strength, and *all* of *my* heart and strength."

Clever Queen's heart was just pounding inside. She nudged Clear Gold to see if she were taking notice. Clear Gold nudged back that she was, but didn't say a word. She couldn't, for Thra kept right on.

"The other day," he said, "I was visiting in Thra Myat Po's house, and it happened to be dinnertime. And Thra Myat Po sat on the floor with his little boy Solomon right beside him, eating from their little table. And that father loved that little boy more than anything else in all the world. Little Solomon loved his daddy too, and as he sat there he snuggled up close and tried to do just what his daddy was doing. 'Solomon,' said his daddy, 'how much do you love me?' And little three-year-old Solomon, who couldn't speak very much, but who understood nearly everything, stretched his chubby little arms out as far as he could get them, and said in his baby talk, 'Dis big.' 'Well, then,' said his daddy, 'if you love me, jump up and get me a drink of water.'

"The words were hardly finished when up jumped the little fellow, and he just ran for all he was worth over to the waterpot. But the waterpot was too high, and he couldn't reach it; then he looked at the tin cup on the post beside it, and it was too high. He couldn't reach that, and for a minute he stood there not knowing just what he ought to do. Then he stood on his very tiptoes, and stretched up his little hand as far as he could, and with his little stomach pressed flat against the post he could just touch the bottom of that tin cup. But he did all he could do, and as he tinkled the bottom of that tin cup against the post with his little fingers he called out with all his strength, 'Daddy! Daddy! Daddy! I can't reach it.'

"When his father, who was looking proudly on, heard the cry of his little boy, who was doing *all* he could for *all* he was worth, his heart was touched, and he went over and lifted the little fellow up in his arms. He lifted him high till his little hands could grasp the cup and dip the water. Then he put little Solomon on the floor, and though, by the time he got to the table the water was half spilled, I saw that father drink that water, and I heard him say, 'It's the sweetest cup of water I've ever tasted in all my life.' "

Clever Queen listened breathlessly. "That was just for me," she breathed to herself. "That was just for me." And all through the rest of that meeting she felt a new comfort and a new strength coming into her heart. "With all of my little strength, and all of my little heart. Yes, I can do that for Jesus, and I will."

There followed a few pictures telling the story of Jesus. And as the scenes of Jesus on the cross were shown, a quartet sang:

> "When I survey the wondrous cross
>   On which the Prince of Glory died,
> My richest gain I count but loss,
>   And pour contempt on all my pride.
>
> "Were the whole realm of nature mine,
>   That were a tribute far too small;
> Love so amazing, so divine,
>   Demands my life, my soul, my all."

There was a hush through that great audience, broken only by a sob here and there. The lights came on, but no one was ashamed to be seen using a handkerchief. Thra asked those who had determined that night to serve God and to keep His commandments to show their love for Him, to stand. There was but the briefest moment of hesitation,

and Clever Queen and Clear Gold stood hand in hand.
Their heads were bowed, their little breasts rose and fell in
quiet sobs. But they did not stand alone. About sixty stood
with them that night and accepted the Lord Jesus as their
Lord and Master. Sixteen were thought, after careful ques-
tioning, to be ready for baptism; but the smaller ones, in-
cluding Clever Queen, were organized into a baptismal
class, where they could study together all the steps for
baptism.

Another happy two years passed, and at the last camp
meeting I attended in Burma just a few months before I
came back to America, Clever Queen and Clear Gold were
baptized.

It was such a happy day! Grandma was there, and
Clever Queen's mother was there, hundreds of people from
the nearby villages were there, to see how the God worshipers baptize. But the old toothless grandma wasn't there.
"No indeed," she said; "I'll not go to see the Daw-ta-kar eat
up Clever Queen. Indeed I won't!"

But Clever Queen knew there was no Daw-ta-kar to
eat her up; she knew that her eyes had been opened and
that she had turned from the darkness to light and from the
power of Satan to the living God, and she was supremely
happy.